STERLING
Test Prep

Organic Chemistry

Semester I

Practice Questions

3rd edition

3   2   1

ISBN-13: 979-8-8855710-3-6

Sterling Test Prep materials are available at quantity discounts.

Contact info@sterling–prep.com

Sterling Test Prep
6 Liberty Square #11
Boston, MA 02109

© 2023 Sterling Test Prep

Published by Sterling Test Prep

 Printed in the U.S.A.

STERLING
Test Prep

Thousands of students use our study aids to achieve academic success!

To achieve a high grade in college organic chemistry, you need to do well on your tests and final exam. This book helps you develop and apply knowledge to quickly choose the correct answers to questions typically tested in the first semester of organic chemistry. Solving targeted practice questions builds your understanding of fundamental concepts and is a more effective strategy than merely memorizing terms.

This book provides targeted practice questions covering organic chemistry topics. Chemistry instructors with years of teaching experience prepared this practice material to build your knowledge and skills crucial for success in an organic chemistry course. Our editorial team reviewed and systematized the content for targeted preparation.

The detailed explanations describe why an answer is correct and – more important for your learning – why another attractive choice is wrong. They provide easy to follow step-by-step solutions and teach the scientific foundations and details of essential organic chemistry topics. Read the explanations carefully to understand how they apply to the question and learn important organic chemistry principles and the relationships between them.

With this practice material you will significantly improve your understanding, test scores, and your grade.

230105gdx

Visit our Amazon store

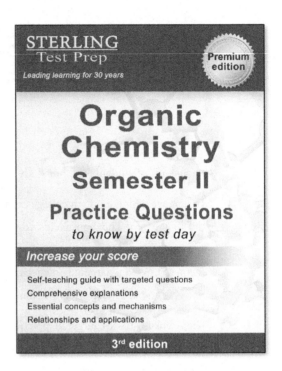

College study aids

Cell and Molecular Biology Review

Organismal Biology Review

Cell and Molecular Biology Practice Questions

Organismal Biology Practice Questions

Physics Review (Part 1 and 2)

Physics Practice Questions (Vol. 1 and 2)

United States History 101

American Government and Politics 101

Environmental Science 101

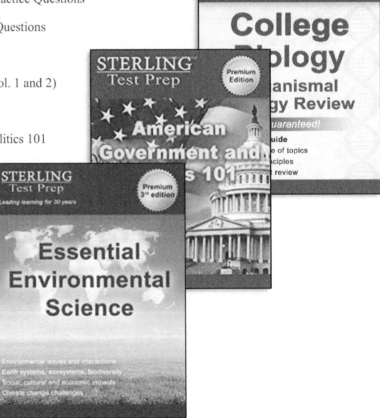

Table of Contents

College Level Examination Program (CLEP)

Visit our Amazon store

Topical Practice Questions

Organic Chemistry Nomenclature

1. Name the structure:

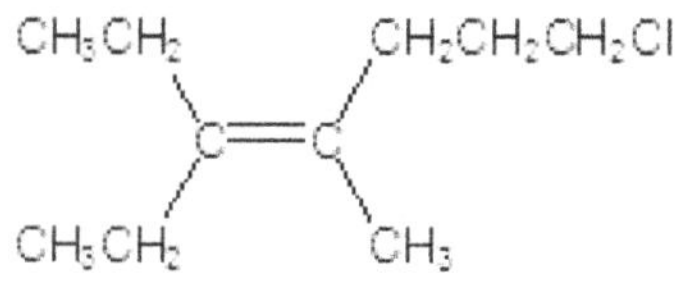

A. *cis*-7-chloro-3-ethyl-4-methyl-3-heptene
B. 1-chloro-3-pentenyl-2-pentene
C. 1-chloro-5-ethyl-4-methyl-3-heptene
D. 7-chloro-3-ethyl-4-methyl-3-heptene
E. *trans*-7-chloro-3-ethyl-4-methyl-3-heptene

2. What is the IUPAC name for the following compound?

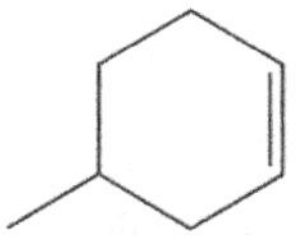

A. 1-methyl-4-cyclohexene
B. 1-methyl-3-cyclohexene
C. 4-methylcyclohexene
D. 5-methylcyclohexene
E. methylcyclohexene

3. Give the formula of the structure below:

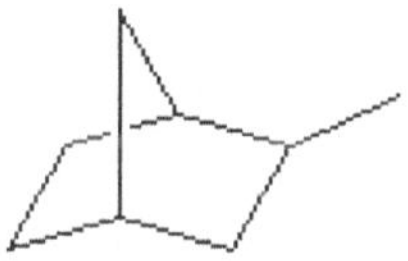

A. C_8H_{14}
B. C_8H_{12}
C. C_8H_{10}
D. C_8H_8
E. C_8H_{16}

4. Which structure is *para*-dibromobenzene?

I. 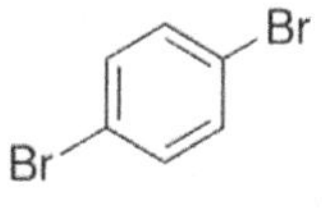

II. 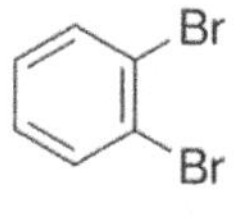

III. 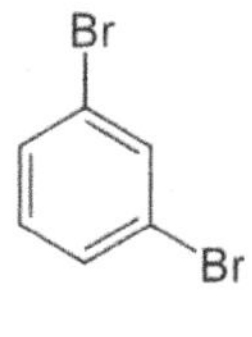

A. I only
B. II only
C. III only
D. I and II only
E. I, II and III

5. Ignoring geometric isomers, what is the IUPAC name for the following compound:

$CH_3–CH=CH–CH_3$

A. but-2-yne

B. but-2-ene

C. butene-3

D. butene-2

E. 2-butyl

6. What is the IUPAC name for the following structure:

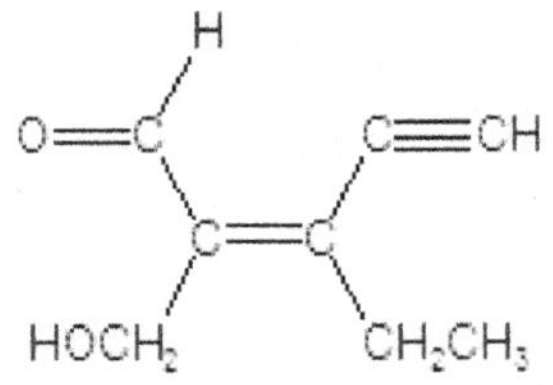

A. (*Z*)-3-ethyl-5-hydroxymethyl-3-penten-1-ynal

B. (*E*)-3-ethyl-5-hydroxymethyl-3-penten-1-ynal

C. (*Z*)-3-ethyl-2-hydroxymethyl-2-penten-4-ynal

D. (*E*)-3-ethyl-2-hydroxymethyl-2-penten-4-ynal

E. 3-ethyl-5-hydroxymethyl-3-penten-1-ynal

7. Give the IUPAC name for the following structure:

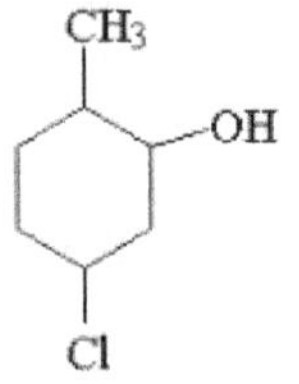

A. 1-chloro-4-methylcyclohexanol

B. 5-chloro-2-methylcyclohexanol

C. 3-chloro-2-methylcyclohexanol

D. 2-methyl-5-chlorocyclohexanol

E. 2-methyl-3-chlorocyclohexanol

8. What is the name of the following compound?

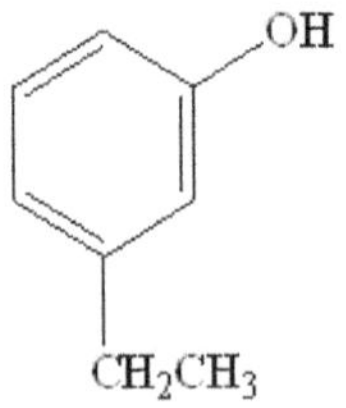

A. *p*-ethylphenol

B. *m*-ethylbenzene

C. *o*-ethylphenol

D. *m*-ethylphenol

E. none of the above

9. Provide the IUPAC name of the compound:

A. *N,N*,2-trimethyl-1-propanamine

B. *N,N*,2-trimethylpropanamine

C. *N,N*,1,1-tetramethylethanamine

D. *N,N*-dimethyl-2-butanamine

E. *N,N*,2-trimethyl-2-propanamine

10. Name the following structure:

A. *cis*-3,4-dimethyl-3-hepten-7-ol

B. *trans*-4,5-dimethyl-4-hepten-1-ol

C. *cis*-4,5-dimethyl-4-hepten-1-ol

D. *trans*-3,4-dimethyl-3-hepten-7-ol

E. *trans*-4,5-dimethyl-4-heptenol

11. What is the systematic name for the following compound?

A. 3-methyl-2-pentanol

B. 4-methyl-3-pentanol

C. 2-methyl-3-pentenol

D. 2-methyl-3-pentanol

E. 3-methyl-3-pentanol

12. Which condensed structural formula below is the isopropyl group?

A.

B.

C.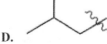

D.

E.

13. Which of the following compounds is named correctly?

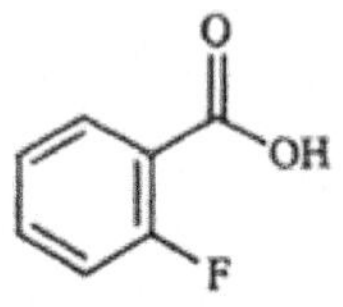

    A. *meta*-fluorobenzoic acid

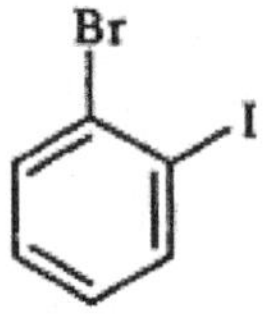

    C. 2-iodo-1-bromobenzene

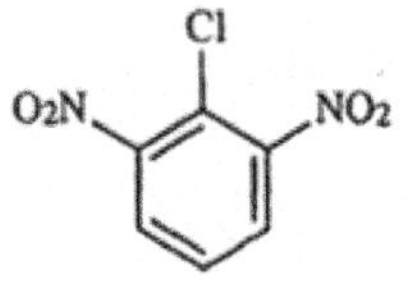

    B. 2,5-dinitro-1-chlorobenzene

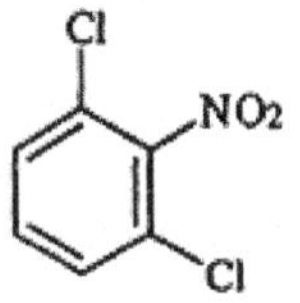

    D. 1,3,dichloro-2-nitrobenzene

    E. None of the above

14. Name the compound shown below.

    A. *cis*-1,3-dichlorocyclohexane

    B. *trans*-1,3-dichlorocyclohexane

    C. *cis*-1,2-dichlorocyclohexane

    D. *trans*-1,2-dichlorocyclohexane

    E. *cis*-1,4-dichlorocyclohexane

15. What is the IUPAC name of the compound shown?

$$CH_3-CH-CH_2-CH-CH_3$$
$$\quad\;\; | \qquad\quad\; |$$
$$\quad\;\; CH_3 \qquad OH$$

    A. 2, 2-dimethyl-4-butanol

    B. 4, 4-dimethyl-2-butanol

    C. 2-methyl-4-pentanol

    D. 4-methyl-2-pentanol

    E. 2-isohexanol

16. What is the IUPAC name of the compound shown below?

    A. (1*R*,4*S*)-1,4-dichloro-1-ethyl-4-methylcyclopentane

    B. (1*R*,3*S*)-1,3-dichloro-1-ethyl-3-methylcyclopentane

    C. (1*S*,3*S*)-1,3-dichloro-1-ethyl-3-methylcyclopentane

    D. (1*R*,3*S*)-1,3-dichloro-1-methyl-3-ethylcyclopentane

    E. (1*S*,3*R*)-1,3-dichloro-3-ethyl-1-methylcyclopentane

17. The compound $CH_3(CH_2)_5CH_3$ is:

    A. heptane   **C.** hexane

    B. hexene   **D.** pentane

                                 E. octene

18. Name the following structure:

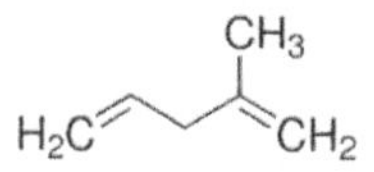

    A. 2-methylene-4-pentene   **C.** 2-methyl-2,4-pentadiene

    B. 4-methylene-2-pentene   **D.** 4-methyl-1,4-pentadiene

                                 E. 2-methyl-1,4-pentadiene

19. The name of the following alkyl group is ~$CH_2CH_2CH_3$:

    A. ethyl   **C.** isopropyl

    B. propyl   **D.** *sec*-butyl

                                 E. butyl

20. What is the complete systematic IUPAC name for the following compound?

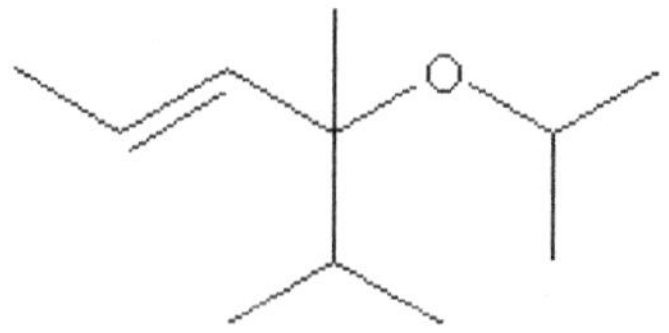

    A. isopropyl-(4-isopropyl-4-methylbut-2-enyl) ether

    B. (*E*)-4-isopropoxy-4,5-dimethylhex-2-ene

    C. 4-(1-methylethoxy)-4-isopropyl-4-methylpent-2-ene

    D. 4-isopropyl-2,4-dimethylhept-5-en-3-ol

    E. 4-isopropyl-4-methylbut-2-en-isopropyl ether

21. The IUPAC name for the compound $H_2C=CH–CH=CH_2$ is:

    A. 1,3-butadiene   **C.** butene-2

    B. butane-1,3   **D.** 1,3-dibutene

                                 E. 2-butyne

22. What is the IUPAC name for salicylic acid shown below:

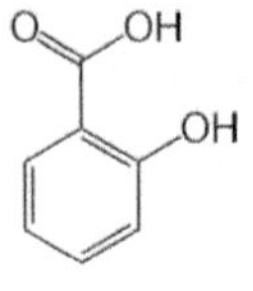

    A. 2-hydroxybenzoic acid   **C.** 1-hydroxybenzoic acid

    B. α-hydroxybenzoic acid   **D.** meta-hydroxybenzoic acid

                                      E. 3-hydroxybenzoic acid

23. What is the common name for the simplest ketone, propanone?

    A. acetal   **C.** carbanone

    B. acetone   **D.** formalin

                                      E. none of the above

24. The name of the compound shown below is:

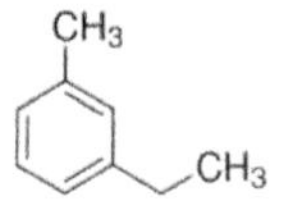

    A. 3-ethyltoluene   **C.** 1-ethyl-4-methylbenzene

    B. 2-ethyltoluene   **D.** 1-ethyl-2-methylbenzene

                                      E. 4-ethyltoluene

25. A compound with the molecular formula C_3H_6 is:

    A. butane   **C.** 2-methylpropane

    B. butyne   **D.** cyclopropane

                                    E. propane

26. What is the correct IUPAC name for the following compound?

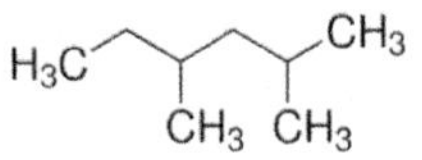

    A. 2-ethyl-4-methylhexane   **C.** 4-ethyl-2-methylhexane

    B. 2,4-dimethylhexane   **D.** 3,5-dimethylheptane

                                    E. *sec*-butylpropane

27. Name the following structure according to IUPAC nomenclature:

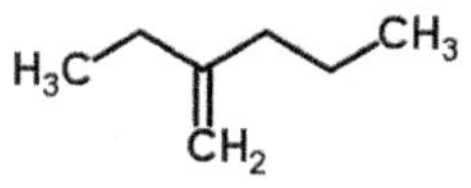

A. 3-ethyl-3-hexene

B. 4-methylenehexane

C. 2-propyl-1-butene

D. 2-ethyl-1-pentene

E. ethyl-propylethene

28. What is the IUPAC name for the following structure?

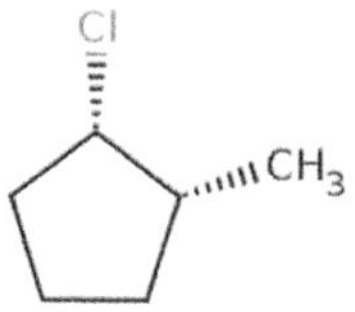

A. *cis*-methylcyclohexane

B. *cis*-1-chloro-2-methylcyclopentane

C. *Z*-chloro-methylcyclohexane

D. *cis*-2-chloro-2-methylcyclohexane

E. *Z*-2-chloro-1-methylcyclohexane

29. The compound below is:

A. pentanone

B. pentanal

C. butanaldehyde

D. pentaketone

E. pentanoic acid

30. Provide the common name of the compound:

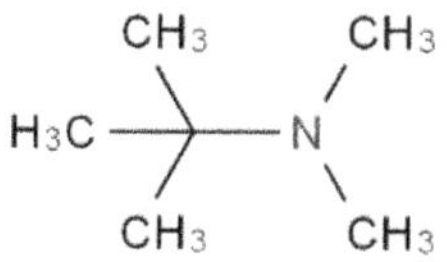

A. neobutyldimethylamine

B. *sec*-butyldimethylamine

C. *tert*-butyldimethylamine

D. isobutyldimethylamine

E. *n*-butyldimethylamine

31. What is the correct IUPAC name for the following compound?

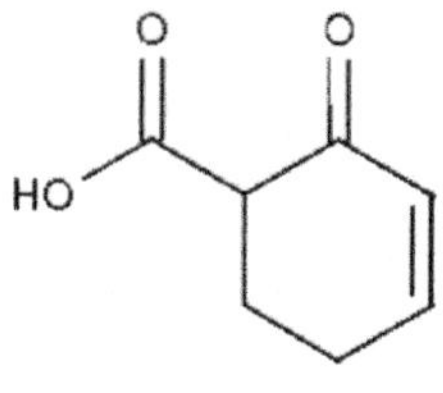

A. 2-oxocyclohex-3-ene-1-carboxylic acid

B. 5-formylcyclohex-2-enone-oic acid

C. 2-formylcyclohex-5-enone

D. 3-oxocyclohex-4-enoic acid

E. 2-oxocyclohex-3-ene carbonate

32. What is the IUPAC name of the compound shown?

- **A.** 3,4,6-trimethylheptane
- **B.** 2,4,5-trimethylheptane

- **C.** 3,5-dimethyl-2-ethylhexane
- **D.** 2-ethyl-3,5-dimethylhexane
- **E.** 5-ethyl-2,4-dimethylhexane

33. What is the IUPAC name for the following structure?

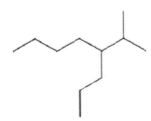

- **A.** 5,6-dimethyl cyclohexane
- **B.** *cis*-1,2-dimethyl cyclohexane

- **C.** *trans*-1,2-dimethyl cyclohexane
- **D.** 1,2-dimethyl cyclohexane
- **E.** none of the above

34. Give the IUPAC name for the following structure:

- **A.** 4-isopropyloctane
- **B.** 5-isopropyloctane

- **C.** 3-ethyl-2-methylheptane
- **D.** 2-methyl-3-ethylheptane
- **E.** 2-methyl-3-propylheptane

35. Which name is NOT correct for IUPAC nomenclature?

- **A.** 2,2-dimethylbutane
- **B.** 2,3-dimethylpentane

- **C.** 2,3,3-trimethylbutane
- **D.** 2,3,4-trimethylpentane
- **E.** All are correct names

36. Which compound has the common name *sec*-butylamine?

- **A.** 1-butanamine
- **B.** 2-butanamine

- **C.** *N*-methyl-1-propanamine
- **D.** *N*-methyl-2-propanamine
- **E.** *N*-ethylethanamine

37. Which of the following is *cis*-2,3-dichloro-2-butene?

A.

C.

B.

D.

E. None of the above

38. Which of the following is the IUPAC name for this compound?

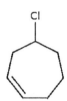

A. 3-ethylhexan-2-one

B. 4-ethylhexan-5-one

C. 3-propylpentan-2-one

D. 3-propylpentan-4-one

E. hexana-3-one

39. Name the structure shown below:

A. 1-chloro-3-cycloheptene

B. 4-chlorocycloheptane

C. 4-chlorocyclohexene

D. 1-chloro-3-cyclohexene

E. 4-chlorocycloheptene

40. Provide the IUPAC name of the compound:

A. 1,1-dimethyl-5-chloropentane

B. 6-chloro-2-methylhexane

C. 1-chloro-5-methylhexane

D. 2-methyl-chloro-heptane

E. 1,1-dichloro-5-methylpentane

41. Ethyl propanoate is a(n):

A. ester

B. alcohol

C. aldehyde

D. carboxyl alcohol

E. amide

42. Provide the common name of the compound:

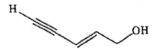

A. isoheptyl chloride

B. *tert*-heptyl chloride

C. neoheptyl chloride

D. *sec*-heptyl chloride

E. n-heptyl chloride

43. What is the IUPAC name of the molecule shown?

$$CH_2=CH-CH_2-CH_2-CH-CH_3$$
$$|$$
$$CH_2$$
$$|$$
$$CH_3$$

A. 2-ethyl-5-hexene

B. 5-ethyl-1-hexene

C. 5-methyl-1-heptene

D. 3-methyl-6-heptene

E. octane

44. Which of the following is NOT a proper condensed structural formula for an alkane?

A. $CH_3CHCH_3CH_2CH_3$

B. $CH_3CH_2CH_2CH_2CH_3$

C. $CH_3CH_3CH_3$

D. $CH_3CH_2CH_2CH_3$

E. CH_3CH_3

45. Which of the following is the IUPAC name for this compound?

A. (*Z*)-pent-3-en-1-yn-5-ol

B. (*E*)-pent-3-en-1-yn-5-ol

C. (*Z*)-pent-2-en-4-yn-1-ol

D. (*E*)-pent-2-en-4-yn-1-ol

E. *Cis*-pent-2-en-4-yn-1-ol

46. What is the name of the following compound: $H_3CCH_2CH_2CH_2CH_2CONH_2$

A. 1-hexanamide

B. hexanamide

C. hexanamine

D. hexamine

E. hexketoneamine

Notes for active learning

Notes for active learning

Covalent Bond

1. Which of the following is a benzylic cation?

A.

C.

B.

D.

E.

2. Which orbitals overlap to create the H–C bond in CH_3^+?

A. s–p
B. s–sp^2

C. sp^3–sp^3
D. sp^2–sp^3
E. s–sp^3

3. Which of the following structures, including formal charges, is correct for diazomethane, CH_2N_2?

A. $H_2C=N^+=N^-$
B. $H_2C=N^+\equiv N^-$

C. $H2C=N^-=N^+$
D. $^-CH_2-N\equiv N:$
E. $H_2C-N^{+3}\equiv N^{-3}$

4. What chemical reaction did German chemist Friedrich Wohler use to synthesize urea for the first time?

A. Heating ammonium cyanide
B. Combining the elements carbon, hydrogen, oxygen, and nitrogen
C. Evaporating urine
D. Heating ammonium cyanate
E. None of the above

5. Which of the following is an allylic cation?

A.

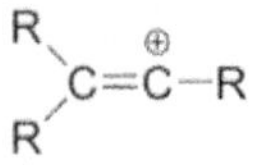

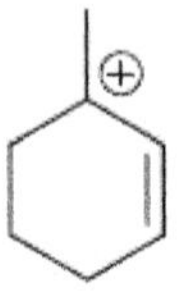

C.

B.

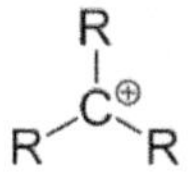

D.

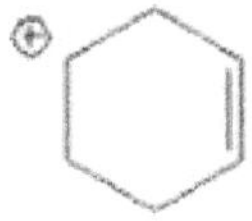

E. $CH_3C^+HCH_3$

6. Which of the following best approximates the C–C–C bond angle of propene?

A. 90°

B. 109°

C. 120°

D. 150°

E. 180°

7. What determines the polarity of a covalent bond?

A. The difference in the number of protons

B. The difference in the number of valence electrons

C. The difference in the atomic size

D. The difference in the electronegativity

E. None of the above

8. What is the molecular geometry of an open-chain noncyclical hydrocarbon with the generic molecular formula C_nH_{2n-2}?

A. trigonal pyramidal

B. trigonal planar

C. tetrahedral

D. linear

E. none of the above

9. Identify the most stable carbocation:

A. $H_2C{=}CH \oplus$

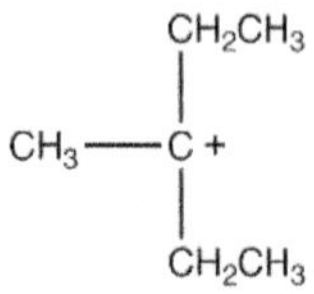

C.

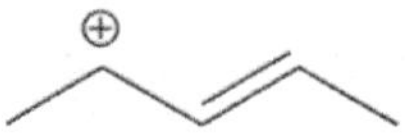

B.

D.

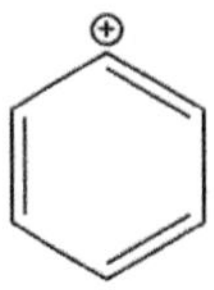

E.

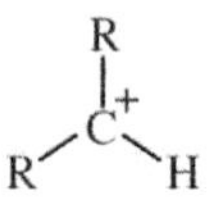

10. Consider the interaction of two hydrogen $1s$ atomic orbitals of the same phase. Which of the statements below is NOT a correct description of this interaction?

    A. The molecular orbital formed is cylindrically symmetric

    B. The molecular orbital formed has a node between the atoms

    C. The molecular orbital formed is lower in energy than a hydrogen $1s$ atomic orbital

    D. A *sigma* bonding molecular orbital is formed

    E. A maximum of two electrons may occupy the molecular orbital formed

11. In *trans*-hept-4-en-2-yne, the shortest carbon-carbon bond is between carbons:

    A. 1 and 2   **C.** 3 and 4

    B. 2 and 3   **D.** 4 and 5

                                E. 5 and 6

12. What two atomic orbitals (or hybrid atomic orbitals) overlap to form the C=C π bond in ethylene?

    A. $C\ sp^2 + C\ p$ **C.** $C\ sp^3 + C\ sp^2$

    B. $C\ sp^2 + C\ sp^2$ **D.** $C\ sp^3 + C\ sp^3$

                                  E. $C\ p + C\ p$

13. Which of the following is the most stable resonance contributor to acetic acid?

$$
\begin{array}{c}
:\!\overset{\displaystyle ..}{O}\!: \\
\|\\
CH_3\!\!-\!\!C\!\!-\!\!\overset{..}{\underset{..}{O}}\!\!-\!\!H
\end{array}
$$

A.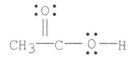

B.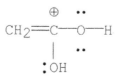

C.

D.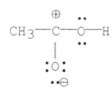

E.
$$
\begin{array}{c}
\overset{\displaystyle \oplus}{}\\
CH_3\!\!-\!\!C\!\!-\!\!\overset{..}{O}\!\!-\!\!H\\
|\\
:\!\overset{}{\underset{\cdot\ominus}{O}}\!:
\end{array}
$$

14. The compound methylamine, CH_3NH_2, contains a C–N bond. In this bond, which of the following best describes the charge on the nitrogen atom?

A. uncharged

B. slightly negative

C. +1

D. slightly positive

E. −1

15. Which of the following molecules is the most polar?

A. acetaldehyde

B. acetic acid

C. ethane

D. ethylene

E. benzene

16. A molecule of acetylene (C_2H_2) has a [   ] geometry and a molecular dipole moment that is [   ].

A. bent, zero

B. linear, nonzero

C. tetrahedral, nonzero

D. bent, nonzero

E. linear, zero

17. Which of the following is NOT a resonance structure of the species shown?

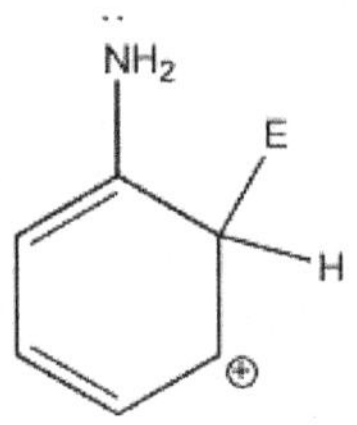

A.

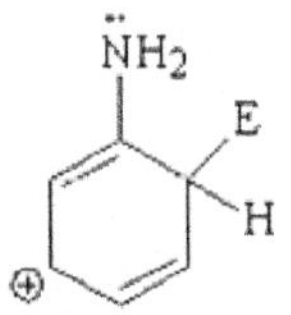

B.

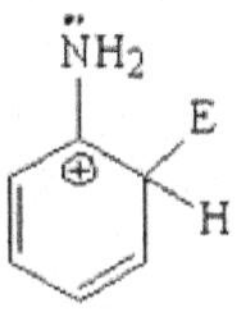

C.

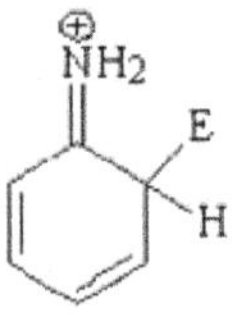

D.

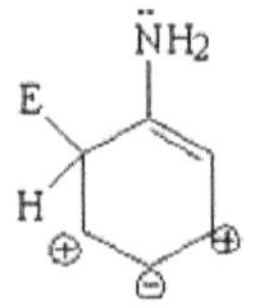

E. All are resonance forms

18. In an aqueous environment, which bond requires the most energy to break?

A. hydrogen

B. dipole-dipole

C. *sigma*

D. ionic

E. *pi*

19. The nitrogen atom of trimethylamine is [   ] hybridized which is reflected in the C–N–C bond angle of [   ]:

A. *sp*, 180°

B. *sp²*, 120°

C. *sp²*, 108°

D. *sp³*, 120°

E. *sp³*, 108°

20. Which of the following statements concerning the cyclic molecule shown is NOT true?

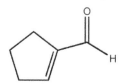

A. It contains a π molecular orbital formed by the overlap of carbon *p* atomic orbitals

B. It contains a σ molecular orbital formed by the overlap of carbon *sp³* hybrid atomic orbitals

C. It contains a σ molecular orbital formed by the overlap of carbon *sp²* hybrid atomic orbitals

D. It contains a π molecular orbital formed by the overlap of a carbon *p* atomic orbital with an oxygen *p* atomic orbital

E. It contains a σ molecular orbital formed by the overlap of a carbon *p* atomic orbital with an oxygen *sp³* atomic orbital

21. Draw a structural formula for cyclohexane, a cyclic saturated hydrocarbon (C_6H_{12}). How many π bonds are in a cyclohexane molecule?

A. 3

B. 4

C. 0

D. 2

E. 6

22. The N–H bond in the ammonium ion, NH_4^+, is formed by the overlap of which two orbitals?

A. *sp²–s*

B. *sp²–sp²*

C. *sp³–sp²*

D. *sp³–sp³*

E. *sp³–s*

23. Among the hydrogen halides, the strongest bond is in [   ], and the longest bond is in [   ]?

A. HI ... HI

B. HI ... HF

C. HF ... HI

D. HF ... HF

E. HCl ... HBr

24. Which of the following is the most stable carbocation?

A.

B.

C.

D.

E.

25. Which of the following is the least stable carbocation? (Use Ph = phenyl group)

A. PhH_2C^+

B. $CH_3CH_2CH_2^+$

C. Ph_3C^+

D. Ph_2HC^+

E. $CH_3CH_2C^+HCH_3$

26. The energy of an sp^3 hybridized orbital for a carbon atom is:

A. lower in energy than the $2s$ and $2p$ atomic orbitals

B. higher in energy than the $2s$ and $2p$ atomic orbitals

C. higher in energy than the $2p$ atomic orbital but lower in energy than the $2s$ atomic orbital

D. higher in energy than the $2s$ atomic orbital but lower in energy than the $2p$ atomic orbital

E. equal in energy to the $2p$ atomic orbital

27. Which of the following pairs are resonance structures?

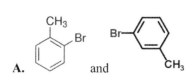

A. and

B. and

C. and

D. and

E. and

28. Due to electron delocalization, the carbon-oxygen bond in acetamide, CH_3CONH_2:

   A. is longer than the carbon-oxygen bond of dimethyl ether, $(CH_3)_2O$
   B. is longer than the carbon-oxygen bond of acetone, $(CH_3)_2CO$
   C. is nonpolar
   D. has more double bond character than the carbon-oxygen bond of acetone, $(CH_3)_2CO$
   E. is formed by overlapping sp^3 orbitals

29. Which of the compounds listed below is linear?

   A. 1,3,5-heptatriene
   B. acetylene
   C. 2-butyne
   D. dichloromethane
   E. 1,3-hexadiene

30. How many single and double bonds are in the benzene molecule (not including the C–H bonds)?

   A. 6 single, 2 double
   B. 5 single, 2 double
   C. 6 single, 0 double
   D. 5 single, 0 double
   E. 6 single, 3 double

31. Determine the number of *pi* bonds in CH_3CN:

A. 0

B. 1

C. 2

D. 3

E. 4

32. Give the hybridization, shape, and bond angle for carbon in ethene:

A. sp^3, tetrahedral, 120°

B. sp^3, tetrahedral, 109.5°

C. sp^2, trigonal planar, 120°

D. sp^2, trigonal planar, 109.5°

E. none of the above

33. C=C, C=O, C=N, and N=N bonds are observed in many organic compounds. However, C=S, C=P, C=Si, and other similar bonds are not often found. What is the most probable explanation for this observation?

A. the comparative sizes of $3p$ atomic orbitals make effective overlap less likely than between two $2p$ orbitals

B. S, P, and Si do not undergo hybridization of orbitals

C. S, P and Si do not form π bonds, lacking occupied p orbitals in their ground state electron configurations

D. carbon does not combine with elements found below the second row of the periodic table

E. none of the above

34. How many σ bonds are in cyclohexane (C_6H_{12}), a saturated cyclic hydrocarbon?

A. 12

B. 14

C. 16

D. 18

E. 20

35. Triethylamine [$(CH_3CH_2)_3N$] is a molecule in which the nitrogen atom is [   ] hybridized, and the C–N–C bond angle is approximately [   ].

A. sp^3 … < 107°

B. sp^3 … 109.5°

C. sp^2 … > 109.5°

D. sp^2 … < 109.5°

E. sp … 109.5°

36. How many distinct and degenerate p orbitals exist in the second electron shell, where n = 2?

A. 3

B. 2

C. 1

D. 0

E. 4

37. Which of the following compounds exhibits the greatest dipole moment?

A. (1*S*,2*S*)-1,2-dichloro-1,2-diphenylethane

B. 1,2-dichlorobutane

C. (1*R*,2*S*)-1,2-dichloro-1,2-diphenylethane

D. (*E*)-1,2-dichlorobutene

E. (*Z*)-1,2-dibromobutene

38. Draw a structural formula for benzene. How many σ bonds are in the molecule?

A. 14

B. 18

C. 6

D. 12

E. 20

39. Which is the formal charge of nitrogen in NH_4?

A. –2

B. –1

C. 0

D. +1

E. +2

40. The nitrogen's lone pair in pyrrolidine is occupying which type of orbital?

A. *s*

B. *sp*^{3}

C. *sp*^{2}

D. *sp*

E. *p*

41. Acetone is a common solvent used in organic chemistry laboratories. Which of the following statements is/are correct regarding acetone?

Acetone

I. One atom is *sp*^{3} hybridized and tetrahedral

II. One atom is *sp*^{2} hybridized and trigonal planar

III. The carbonyl carbon contains an unshared pair of electrons

A. I only

B. II only

C. I and II only

D. II and III only

E. I, II and III

42. Which of the following molecules represents the most stable carbocation?

A. $H_2C{=}C(H){-}CH_2^{\oplus}$

B. $H_2C{=}C(CH_3){-}CH_2^{\oplus}$

C. $CH_3CH{=}C(H){-}CH_2^{\oplus}$

D. $CH_3CH_2CH{=}C(H){-}CH_2^{\oplus}$

E. $CH_3C(CH_3){=}C(H){-}CH_2^{\oplus}$

43. Which of the following pairs are resonance structures?

A. (2-methyl-propene structure) and (cyclopropane triangle)

B. and $CH_3{-}C(={\ddot{O}}){-}H$

C. $CH_3{-}C(={\ddot{O}}){-}H$ and

D. $CH_3{-}C(={O}){-}H$ and $CH_3{-}\overset{\ominus}{C}(H){-}\overset{\oplus}{\ddot{O}}$

E. $H_3C{-}\ddot{O}{-}CH_3$ and $H_3C{-}OH$

44. Which of the following is closest to the C–O–C bond angle in CH_3–O–CH_3?

A. 109.5°

B. 90°

C. 180°

D. 120°

E. 140°

45. Identify the number of carbon atoms for each hybridization in the molecule?

$$O=CH-CH_2-CH=C=C=CH_2$$

	sp	*sp²*	*sp³*
A.	1	4	1
B.	2	3	1
C.	0	3	3
D.	1	3	2
E.	2	3	2

46. Identify the correctly drawn arrows:

A.

B.

C.

D.

E.

47. Triethylamine, $(CH_3CH_2)_3N$, is a molecule in which the nitrogen atom is [   ] hybridized and the molecular shape is [   ].

A. sp^3 … trigonal pyramidal   **C.** sp^2 … tetrahedral

B. sp^3 … tetrahedral   **D.** sp^2 … trigonal planar

   E. sp … bent

48. Which of the following is the most stable cation?

A.

B.

C.

D.

E.

Notes for active learning

Stereochemistry

1. Butene, C_4H_8, is a hydrocarbon with one double bond. How many isomers are there of butene?

    A. two

    B. three

    C. four

    D. five

    E. no isomers

2. Which of the following compounds has an asymmetric center?

A.

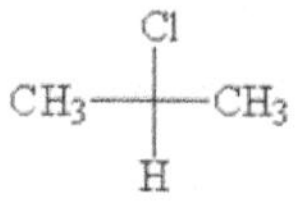

$$CH_3\!-\!\!\overset{\displaystyle Cl}{\underset{\displaystyle H}{|}}\!\!-\!CH_3$$

B.

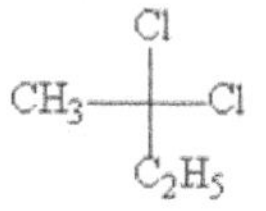

$$CH_3\!-\!\!\overset{\displaystyle Cl}{\underset{\displaystyle C_2H_5}{|}}\!\!-\!Cl$$

C.

$$Cl\!-\!\!\overset{\displaystyle Cl}{\underset{\displaystyle CH_3}{|}}\!\!-\!H$$

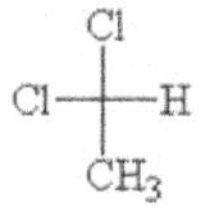

D.

$$CH_3\!-\!\!\overset{\displaystyle Cl}{\underset{\displaystyle Br}{|}}\!\!-\!H$$

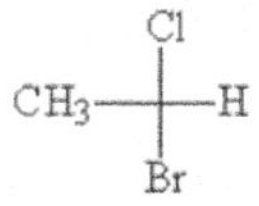

E.

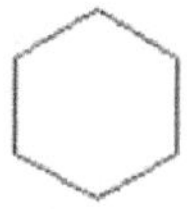

3. How many stereoisomers are possible for the structure below?

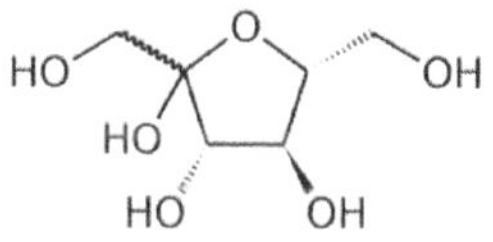

A. 2

B. 4

C. 8

D. 16

E. 32

4. *Cis-trans* isomerism occurs when:

    A. each carbon in an alkene double bond has two different substituent groups

    B. the carbons in the *para* position of an aromatic ring have the same substituent groups

    C. a branched alkane has a halogen added to two adjacent carbon atoms

    D. an alkene is hydrated according to Markovnikov's Rule

    E. hydrogen is added to both carbon atoms in a double bond

5. What is the relationship between the following molecules?

A. different molecules

B. enantiomers

C. identical

D. isomers

E. diastereomers

6. What is the relationship between the structures shown below?

A. geometric isomers

B. conformational isomers

C. constitutional isomers

D. diastereomers

E. enantiomers

7. What is the relationship between the following compounds?

A. conformational isomers

B. diastereomers

C. superimposable without bond rotation

D. constitutional isomers

E. enantiomers

8. Which of the following is NOT true of enantiomers?

A. Enantiomers have the same chemical reactivity with non-chiral reagents

B. Enantiomers have the same density

C. Enantiomers have the same melting point

D. Enantiomers have the same boiling point

E. Enantiomers have the same direction of specific rotation

9. When two compounds consist of the same number and kind of atoms but differ in molecular structure are:

    A. hydrocarbons

    B. isomers

    C. homologs

    D. isotopes

    E. allotropes

10. Identify the relationship between the compounds:

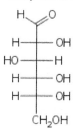

    A. constitutional isomers

    B. configurational isomers

    C. identical

    D. conformational isomers

    E. none of the above

11. Which of the following carbons in the molecule below are chiral carbons?

$$\underset{1}{CH_2}-\underset{2}{C}-\underset{3}{CH}-\underset{4}{CH}-\underset{5}{CH_2OH}$$

with substituents OH, O (double bond), OH, OH

    A. carbons 1 and 5

    B. carbons 3 and 4

    C. carbons 2, 3 and 4

    D. all carbons are chiral

    E. none of the carbon atoms are chiral

12. How many different stereoisomers can the following compound have?

D-glucose

    A. 2

    B. 4

    C. 8

    D. 16

    E. 32

13. $CH_3–CH_2–O–H$ and $CH_3–O–CH_3$ are a pair of:

A. isomers

B. epimers

C. anomers

D. allotropes

E. geometric isomers

14. What is the relationship between the two structures shown below?

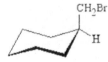 and

A. conformational isomers

B. configurational isomers

C. enantiomers

D. constitutional isomers

E. not isomers

15. Among the butane conformers, which occur at energy minima on a graph of potential energy versus dihedral angle?

A. *anti*

B. eclipsed

C. *gauche*

D. eclipsed and *gauche*

E. *gauche* and *anti*

16. How many isomers exist for dibromobenzene, $C_6H_4Br_2$?

A. 0

B. 1

C. 2

D. 3

E. 4

17. How many isomers are there of butane, C_4H_{10}?

A. 3

B. 4

C. 1 (no isomers)

D. 2

E. 5

18. What is the relationship between the following compounds?

 and

A. constitutional isomers

B. structural isomers

C. geometric isomers

D. conformational isomers

E. positional isomers

19. Which of the following compounds are isomers?

I. $CH_3CH_2OCH_3$ III. $CH_2COHCH_2CH_3$

II. $CH_3CH_2CH_2OH$ IV. $CH_3CH_2OCH_2CH_3$

A. I and II only
B. II and III only

C. III and IV only
D. I, II and III only
E. I, II, III and IV

20. The cause of *cis-trans* isomerism is:

A. short length of the double bond
B. strength of the double bond

C. lack of rotation of the double bond
D. stability of the double bond
E. vibration of the double bond

21. Which of the following compounds is an isomer of $CH_3CH_2CH_2CH_2OH$?

A. $CH_3CH_2CH_2OH$
B. $CH_3(OH)CHCH_3$

C. $CH_3CH_2CH_2CHO$
D. $CH_3CH_2(OH)CHCH_3$
E. CH_3OH

22. If two of the hydrogen atoms in ethylene, $H_2C=CH_2$, are replaced by one chlorine atom and one fluorine atom to form chlorofluoroethene, C_2H_2ClF, how many different chlorofluoro-ethene isomers are there?

A. 4
B. 3

C. 2
D. 1
E. 6

23. In the Fischer projection below, what are the configurations of the two asymmetric centers?

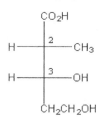

A. 2*S*, 3*S*
B. 2*S*, 3*R*

C. 2*R*, 3*S*
D. 2*R*, 3*R*
E. Cannot be determined

24. Which of the following terms best describes the pair of compounds shown?

A. same molecule

B. conformational isomers

C. enantiomers

D. diastereomers

E. configurational isomers

25. If two of the hydrogen atoms in ethylene, $H_2C=CH_2$, are replaced by two chlorine atoms to form dichloroethylene, how many different dichloroethylene isomers are there?

A. 3

B. 4

C. 1

D. 2

E. 6

26. The enantiomer of the compound below is:

```
      CHO
       |
  H — C — OH
       |
  H — C — OH
       |
      CH₂OH
```

A.
```
      CHO
       |
  H — C — OH
       |
 HO — C — H
       |
      CH₂OH
```

C.
```
      CHO
       |
 HO — C — H
       |
  H — C — OH
       |
      CH₂OH
```

B.
```
      CHO
       |
 HO — C — H
       |
 HO — C — H
       |
      CH₂OH
```

D.
```
      CHO
       |
  H — C — OH
       |
  H — C — OH
       |
      CH₂OH
```

E. none of the above

27. Which of the statements correctly describes an achiral molecule?

    A. The molecule has an enantiomer

    B. The molecule may be a *meso* form

    C. The molecule has a non superimposable mirror image

    D. The molecule exhibits optical activity when it interacts with plane-polarized light

    E. None of the above

28. Which of the following statements does NOT correctly describe *cis*-1,2-dimethylcyclopentane?

    A. Its diastereomer is *trans*-1,2-dimethylcyclopentane

    B. It contains two asymmetric carbons

    C. It is achiral

    D. It is a *meso* compound

    E. It has an enantiomer

29. How many structural isomers of $C_4H_8Cl_2$ exhibit optical activity?

    A. 0   **C.** 2

    B. 1   **D.** 3

                                   E. 4

30. How many chiral carbon atoms are in this structure?

$$CH_2-CH-CH-CHCH_3$$
$$\quad|\quad\ |\quad\ \ |\quad\ \ |$$
$$\ \ OH\ \ OH\ \ Br\ \ \ Cl$$

    A. 6   **C.** 3

    B. 5   **D.** 4

                                   E. 2

31. Which of the following is a true statement?

    A. A mixture of achiral compounds is optically inactive

    B. Molecules that possess a single chirality center of the *S* configuration are levorotatory

    C. Achiral molecules are *meso*

    D. Chiral molecules possess a plane of symmetry

    E. Molecules that possess 2 or more chiral centers are chiral

32. Which of the following best describes the geometry of the carbon-carbon double bond in the alkene below?

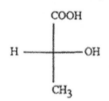

A. *E*	**C.** *cis*
B. *Z*	**D.** *R*
	E. *S*

33. Which of the following compounds share the same absolute configuration?

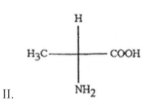

A. I and III only	**C.** I and IV only
B. I and II only	**D.** II, III and IV only
	E. II and IV only

34. What is the correct IUPAC name for the following structure?

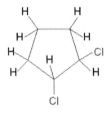

A. *trans*-1,2-dichlorocyclopentane	**C.** *cis*-1,2-dichlorocyclopentane
B. 1,2-dichlorocyclopentane	**D.** *trans*-dichlorocyclopentane
	E. Z-dichlorocyclopentane

35. Which of the following compounds is NOT chiral?

A. 1,2-dichlorobutane

B. 1,4-dibromobutane

C. 2,3-dibromobutane

D. 1,3-dibromobutane

E. 1-bromo-2-chlorobutane

36. The specific rotation of a pure enantiomeric substance is –6.30°. What is the percentage of this enantiomer in a mixture with an observed specific rotation of –3.15°?

A. 75%

B. 80%

C. 25%

D. 50%

E. 0%

37. Which of the following is a result of the reaction below?

(*S*)-3-bromo-3-methylhexane + HCN

A. loss of optical activity

B. mutarotation

C. retention of optical activity

D. inversion of absolute configuration

E. epimerization

38. If two chlorine atoms replace two of the hydrogen atoms in butane, how many different dichlorobutane constitutional isomers can there be?

A. 4

B. 3

C. 2

D. 1

E. 6

39. How many asymmetric centers are present in the compound shown below?

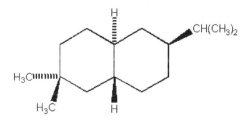

A. 1

B. 2

C. 3

D. 4

E. 5

40. What is the relationship between the structures shown below?

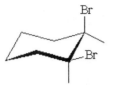

A. identical compounds

B. configurational isomers

C. diastereomers

D. enantiomers

E. constitutional isomers

41. Which of the following statement(s) for the compound *meso*-tartaric acid is/are true?

I. achiral

II. the polarimeter reads a zero deflection

III. racemic mixture

A. I only

B. II only

C. III only

D. I and II only

E. II and III only

42. Which of the following molecules are identical?

I.   II.   III.

A. I and II

B. I and III

C. II and III

D. I, II and III

E. None of the above

43. Which of the following molecules contains a chiral carbon?

A.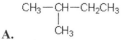
$CH_3-CH-CH_2CH_3$
     $|$
     CH_3

C.
$CH_3-C-CH_2CH_3$
        $\|$
        O

B.
$CH_3-CH-CH_2CH_3$
        $|$
        OH

D.
$CH_3-CH-CH_3$
        $|$
        OH

E. none of the above

44. What is the relationship between the following compounds?

CH_3
$H\cdots C\cdots Cl$ and
CH_3

CH_3
$C\cdots H$
$H\ CH_2Cl$

A. conformational isomers

B. constitutional isomers

C. diastereomers

D. enantiomers

E. identical

45. Which of the following statements about *cis-* / *trans*-isomers is NOT correct?

A. Conversion between *cis–* and *trans*-isomers occurs by rotation around the double bond

B. In the *trans*-isomer, the groups of interest, are on opposite sides across the double bond

C. In the *cis*-isomer, the reference groups, are on the same side of the double bond

D. There are no *cis-* / *tran*-isomers in alkynes

E. There are no *cis* / *trans* isomers in alkanes

46. Which of the following best describes the geometry about the carbon-carbon double bond in the alkene below?

Cl
Br
H
Cl

A. *E*

B. *Z*

E. *R*

C. *cis*

D. *S*

47. Which of the following is a structural isomer of 2-methylbutane?

A. *n*-propane

B. 2-methylpropane

C. *n*-butane

D. *n*-pentane

E. *n*-heptane

Notes for active learning

Molecular Structure and Spectra

1. In the proton NMR, in what region of the spectrum does one typically observe hydrogens bound to the aromatic ring?

A. 1.0-1.5 ppm   **C.** 4.5-5.5 ppm

B. 2.0-3.0 ppm   **D.** 6.0-8.0 ppm

                               E. 8.0-9.0 ppm

2. ^{1}H nuclei located near electronegative atoms are [   ] relative to ^{1}H nuclei not near them.

A. coupled   **C.** shielded

B. split   **D.** deshielded

                 E. none of the above

3. Which compound is expected to show intense IR absorption at 1,715 cm^{-1}?

A. $(CH_3)_2CHNH_2$ **C.** 2-methylhexane

B. hex-1-yne   **D.** $(CH_3)_2CHCO_2H$

                 E. $CH_3CH_2CH_2COH_2CH_3$

4. Free-radical chlorination of propane gives two isomeric monochlorides: 1-chloropropane and 2-chloropropane. How many NMR signals does each of these compounds display, respectively?

A. 3, 2   **C.** 2, 2

B. 3, 3   **D.** 2, 3

                 E. None of the above

5. Which of the following transitions is usually observed in the UV spectra of ketones?

A. n to π^* **C.** σ to n

B. n to π **D.** σ to σ^*

                 E. n to σ^*

6. What is the relative area of each peak in a quartet spin-spin splitting pattern?

A. 1:1:1:1   **C.** 1:2:1

B. 1:4:4:1   **D.** 1:2:2:1

                 E. 1:3:3:1

7. Which NMR signal represents the most deshielded proton?

A. δ 2.0   C. δ 6.5

B. δ 3.8   D. δ 7.3

                                             E. δ 4.5

8. The mass spectrum of alcohols often fails to exhibit detectable M peaks, instead showing relatively large [   ] peaks.

A. M+1   C. M–16

B. M+2   D. M–17

                                             E. M–18

9. In ^{1}H NMR, protons on the α-carbon of amines typically resonate between:

A. 0.5 and 1.0 ppm   C. 3.0 and 4.0 ppm

B. 2.0 and 3.0 ppm   D. 6.0 and 7.0 ppm

                                             E. 9.0 and 10.0 ppm

10. A researcher recorded the NMR spectra of each of the following compounds. Ignoring chemical shifts, which possesses a spectrum significantly different from the others?

A. 1,1,2-tribromobutane   C. 3,3-dibromoheptane

B. bromobutane   D. dibutyl ether

                                             E. the spectra are similar

11. Which compound(s) show(s) intense IR absorption at 1680 cm^{-1}?

I.

II.

III.

A. I only   C. III only

B. II only   D. II and III only

                                             E. I, II and III

12. What is the relationship between H$_a$ and H$_b$ in the following structure?

A. diastereotopic   C. homotopic

B. enantiotopic   D. isotopic

                                             E. conformers

13. Which of the following compounds gives the greatest number of proton NMR peaks?

A. 3,3-dichloropentane

B. 4,4-dichloroheptane

C. 1-chlorobutane

D. 1,4-dichlorobutane

E. dichloromethane

14. Where would one expect to find the ^1H NMR signal for the carboxyl group's hydrogen in propanoic acid?

A. δ 4.1-5.6 ppm

B. δ 10-13 ppm

C. δ 8-9 ppm

D. δ 6.1-7.8 ppm

E. δ 9.5-10 ppm

15. While the carbonyl stretching frequency for simple aldehydes, ketones, and carboxylic acids is about 1710 cm^{-1}, the carbonyl stretching frequency for acid chlorides is about:

A. 1700 cm^{-1}

B. 1735 cm^{-1}

C. 1800 cm^{-1}

D. 1660 cm^{-1}

E. 2200 cm^{-1}

16. A clear liquid is subjected to infrared spectroscopy and produces a spectrum with a prominent, broad peak at approximately 3000 cm^{-1} and a sharp peak at 1710 cm^{-1}, as well as several smaller peaks between 1420 cm^{-1} and 940 cm^{-1}. This substance is most likely:

A. ketone

B. carboxylic acid

C. alcohol

D. aldehyde

E. anhydride

17. Which of the following laboratory techniques is used primarily as a compound identification procedure?

A. extraction

B. NMR spectroscopy

C. crystallization

D. distillation

E. none of the above

18. While the carbonyl stretching frequency for simple aldehydes, ketones, and carboxylic acids is about 1710 cm^{-1}, the carbonyl stretching frequency for esters is about:

A. 1660 cm^{-1}

B. 1700 cm^{-1}

C. 1735 cm^{-1}

D. 1800 cm^{-1}

E. 2200 cm^{-1}

19. A compound with nine carbon atoms produces a single NMR signal. Which is a structural formula for the compound?

A. $(CH_3)_3CCCl_2C(CH_3)_3$

B. $(CH_3)_2CHCH_2CH_2CH(CH_3)CH_2CH_3$

C. $(CH_3)_2CHCH_2(CH_2)_4CH_3$

D. $CH_3(CH_2)_7CH_3$

E. None of the above

20. In mass spectrometry plots, the relative abundance is the unit along the *y*-axis in a mass spectrum. What are the units on the *x*-axis?

A. mass / charge (m/z)

B. mass (m)

C. molecular weight (amu)

D. frequency (ν)

E. wavelength (λ)

21. How many nuclear spin states are allowed for the ^1H nucleus?

A. 1

B. 2

C. 3

D. 4

E. 10

22. Infrared spectroscopy provides a scientist with information about:

A. molecular weight

B. distribution of protons

C. functional group

D. conjugation

E. polarity

23. In the mass spectrum of 3,3-dimethyl-2-butanone, the base peak occurs at *m/z*:

A. 43

B. 58

C. 84

D. 85

E. 100

24. The protons marked H_a and H_b in the molecule below are:

A. diastereotopic

B. heterotopic

C. homotopic

D. enantiotopic

E. endotopic

25. Which of the following compounds is NOT IR active?

A. Cl_2

B. CO

C. $CH_3CH_2CH_2OH$

D. CH_3Br

E. HCN

26. Which sequence correctly ranks the regions of the electromagnetic spectrum in order of increasing energy?

      1) infrared   2) ultraviolet   3) radio wave

A. $3 < 1 < 2$ **C.** $2 < 1 < 3$

B. $3 < 2 < 1$ **D.** $1 < 3 < 2$

                                       E. $1 < 2 < 3$

27. In the UV-visible spectrum of (*E*)-1,3,5-hexatriene, the lowest energy absorption corresponds to a:

A. π to σ^* transition   **C.** σ to π transition

B. σ to σ^* transition   **D.** σ to π^* transition

                                       E. π to π^* transition

28. What type of spectroscopy would be the LEAST useful in distinguishing dimethyl ether from bromoethane?

A. UV spectroscopy   **C.** IR spectroscopy

B. mass spectrometry   **D.** ^{1}H NMR spectroscopy

                                       E. ^{13}C NMR spectroscopy

29. What 1H NMR spectral data is expected for the compound shown?

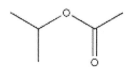

A. 4.9 (1H, sextet), 4.3 (3H, s), 3.0 (6H, d)   **C.** 4.3 (1H, septet), 3.3 (3H, s), 1.2 (6H, d)

B. 3.6 (3H, s), 2.8 (3H, septet), 1.2 (6H, d)   **D.** 3.8 (1H, septet), 2.2 (3H, s), 1.0 (6H, d)

                                                E. 2.8 (1H, septet), 2.2 (3H, s), 1.0 (6H, d)

30. Which of the following compounds absorbs the longest wavelength of UV-visible light?

A. (*Z*)-1,3-hexadiene   **C.** (*Z*)-but-2-ene

B. hex-1-ene   **D.** (*E*)-but-2-ene

                                         E. (*E*)-1,3,5-hexatriene

31. Which of the following compounds generates only one signal on its ^{1}H NMR spectrum?

A. *tert*-butyl alcohol   **C.** toluene

B. 1,2-dibromoethane   **D.** methanol

                                         E. phenol

32. Methyl salicylate and aspirin exhibit a strong absorption for IR at 1,735 cm^{-1}. This absorption indicates:

    A. ester

    B. aromatic ring

    C. alcohol

    D. phenol

    E. amine

33. Absorption of what type of electromagnetic radiation results in electronic transitions?

    A. X-rays

    B. radio waves

    C. microwaves

    D. ultraviolet light

    E. infrared light

34. Which of the following is NOT true?

    A. NMR spectroscopy utilizes magnetic fields

    B. IR spectroscopy utilizes light of wavelength 200-400 nm

    C. UV spectroscopy utilizes transitions in electron states

    D. Mass spectrometry utilizes fragmentation of the sample

    E. IR spectroscopy is useful in the absorption region of 1500 to 3500 cm^{-1}

35. The IR absorption at 1710 cm^{-1} indicates which of the following functional groups?

    A. carbon-carbon double bond

    B. ketone

    C. alcohol

    D. ether

    E. sulfide

36. A compound with a broad, deep IR absorption at 3300 cm^{-1} indicates the presence of:

    A. acyl halide

    B. alcohol

    C. alkene

    D. ketone

    E. alkyne

Notes for active learning

Notes for active learning

Alkanes and Alkyl Halides

1. A nucleophile is:

A. an oxidizing agent

B. electron deficient

C. a Lewis base

D. a Lewis acid

E. none of the above

2. Identify the number of tertiary carbons in the following structure:

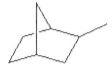

A. 4

B. 5

C. 2

D. 3

E. 6

3. If the concentration of ⁻OH doubles in a reaction with bromopropane, then the reaction rate:

A. quadruples

B. doubles

C. remains the same

D. is halved

E. none of the above

4. The rate of an S_N1 reaction depends on:

A. the concentration of the nucleophile and electrophile

B. neither the concentration of the nucleophile nor the electrophile

C. the concentration of the nucleophile only

D. the concentration of the electrophile only

E. none of the above

5. Which of the following properties is NOT characteristic of alkanes?

A. They are tasteless and colorless

B. They are nontoxic

C. Their melting points increase with molecular weight

D. They are generally less dense than water

E. They have strong hydrogen bonds

6. Predict the most likely mechanism for the reaction shown below:

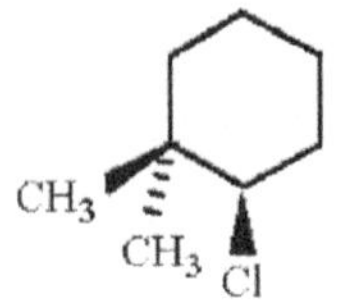

+ $NaOCH_3$ / CH_3OH → ?

    A. E_2 **C.** S_N2

    B. E_1 **D.** S_N1

                                    E. Cannot be determined

7. An alkyl halide forms a more stable carbocation than the carbocation formed from isopropyl bromide. Which of the following alkyl halides forms the most stable carbocation?

    A. *n*-propyl chloride   **C.** methyl chloride

    B. *tert*-butyl chloride   **D.** ethyl chloride

                                      E. propyl chloride

8. Which of the following reactions is most likely to proceed by an S_N2 mechanism?

    A. *t*-butyl iodide with ethanol   **C.** 2-bromo-2-methyl pentane with HCl

    B. 2-bromo-3-methyl pentane with methanol   **D.** 1-bromopropane with NaOH

                                        E. None of the above

9. Which of the following molecules can rotate freely around its carbon-carbon bond?

    A. acetylene   **C.** ethane

    B. cyclopropane   **D.** ethylene

                                      E. none of the above

10. The rate of an S_N2 reaction depends on:

    A. neither the concentration of the nucleophile nor the substrate

    B. the concentration of the nucleophile and the substrate

    C. the concentration of the substrate only

    D. the concentration of the nucleophile only

    E. none of the above

11. The heat of combustion of propane is –530 kcal/mol. A reasonable approximation for the heat of combustion for heptane is:

    A. –432 kcal/mol   **C.** –865 kcal/mol

    B. –682 kcal/mol   **D.** –1158 kcal/mol

                                    E. None of the above

12. Which compound is least soluble in water?

A.

C.

B.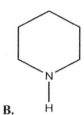

D.

E.

13. Which of the following statements best describes the mechanism of the unimolecular elimination of *tert*-butyl chloride with ethanol?

    A. The reaction is a concerted single-step process

    B. The reaction involves homolytic cleavage of the C–Cl bond

    C. The rate-determining step is the formation of $(CH_3)_3C\cdot$

    D. The rate-determining step is the formation of $(CH_3)_3C^+$

    E. None of the above

14. Which of the following best describes the process of an S_N1 reaction in which the leaving group is on a chiral carbon atom?

    A. inversion of stereochemistry

    B. double inversion of stereochemistry

    C. racemic mixture

    D. retention of stereochemistry

    E. none of the above

15. Which of the following is true regarding S_N1 and S_N2 reactions?

    A. The rates of S_N1 reactions depend mainly on steric factors, while the rates of S_N2 reactions depend mostly on electronic factors

    B. S_N1 reactions proceed more readily with a tertiary alkyl halide substrate, while S_N2 reactions proceed more readily with a primary alkyl halide substrate

    C. S_N1 and S_N2 reactions produce rearrangement products

    D. S_N1 reactions proceed *via* a carbocation intermediate, while S_N2 reactions proceed *via* a carbocation intermediate under certain conditions

    E. S_N1 reactions proceed more readily with a polar aprotic solvent, while S_N2 reactions proceed more readily with a polar protic solvent

16. Which of the compounds listed below has the lowest boiling point?

    A. 3-methylheptane

    B. 2,4-dimethylhexane

    C. octane

    D. 2,2,4-trimethylpentane

    E. decane

17. Which of the following is NOT a feature of S_N2 reactions?

    A. single-step mechanism

    B. pentacoordinate transition state

    C. bimolecular kinetics

    D. carbocation intermediate

    E. nucleophilic substitution

18. Which conformer is at a local energy minimum on the potential energy diagram in the chair-chair interconversion of cyclohexane?

    A. boat

    B. twist-boat

    C. half-chair

    D. planar

    E. fully eclipsed

19. If propane was reacted with Cl_2 in the presence of UV light, what products form, and what are their approximate percentages?

    A. Propyl chloride yields 100%

    B. Propyl chloride yields 42%, and isopropyl chloride yields 58%

    C. Propyl chloride yields 75%, and isopropyl chloride yields 25%

    D. Propyl chloride yields 90%, and isopropyl chloride yields 10%

    E. None of the above

20. What is true about an S_N1 reaction?

> I. A carbocation intermediate is formed
>
> II. The rate determining step is bimolecular
>
> III. The mechanism has two steps

A. I only

B. II only

C. I and II only

D. I and III only

E. I, II and III

21. The most stable conformational isomer of 1,2-dibromoethane is:

A. eclipsed, *anti*

B. staggered, *gauche*

C. staggered, *anti*

D. eclipsed, *gauche*

E. staggered, eclipsed

22. What is the most likely mechanism for the reaction between 1-bromobutane and sodium cyanide?

A. E_1

B. E_2

C. S_N1

D. S_N2

E. S_N1 and S_N2

23. Which of the following alkyl halogens reacts the fastest with NaOH?

A. *t*-butyl bromide

B. *t*-butyl iodide

C. *t*-butyl fluoride

D. *t*-butyl chloride

E. *t*-butyl cyanide

24. Acetate can react with a tertiary alkyl chloride to form an ester. The reaction occurs more rapidly in water than in dimethylsulfoxide (DMSO) because water stabilizes the following:

A. intermediate racemates

B. configuration inversion

C. carbocation intermediate

D. acetate

E. anion intermediate

25. Ethers can be formed from ethyl bromide in a reaction whereby the incoming $^-$OR group represents a(n):

A. substrate

B. electrophile

C. nucleophile

D. leaving group

E. solvent

26. Which of the following compounds can most easily undergo E_1 and S_N2 reactions?

A. $(CH_3CH_2CH_2)_2CHBr$

B. $(CH_3CH_2CH_2)_3CBr$

C. $(CH_3CH_2CH_2)_3CCH_2Cl$

D. $(CH_3CH_2CH_2)_2CHCN$

E. $CH_3CH_2CH_2CH_2Br$

27. Which of the following molecules has the lowest boiling point?

A. *cis*-2-pentene

B. 2-pentyne

C. pentane

D. neopentane

E. 3-pentanol

28. Which of the following is the most stable conformer of *trans*-1-isopropyl-3-methylcyclohexane?

A. methyl and isopropyl are axial

B. methyl and isopropyl are equatorial

C. methyl is axial, and isopropyl is equatorial

D. methyl is equatorial, and isopropyl is axial

E. none of the above

29. Which of the following compounds readily undergoes E_1, S_N1 and E_2 reactions, but not S_N2 reactions?

A. $(CH_3CH_2CH_2)_3CBr$

B. $CH_3CH_2CH_2CH_3$

C. $(CH_3CH_2)_3COH$

D. $CH_3CH_2CH_2CH_2Br$

E. none of the above

30. The complete combustion of one mole of nonane in oxygen would produce [   ] moles of CO_2 and [   ] moles of H_2O?

A. 9 … 10

B. 9 … 9

C. 9 … 4.5

D. 4.5 … 4.5

E. 4.5 … 9

31. Halogenation of alkanes proceeds by the mechanism shown below:

I. $Br_2 + h\nu \rightarrow 2\ Br\bullet$

II. $Br\bullet + RH \rightarrow HBr + R\bullet$

III. $R\bullet + Br_2 \rightarrow RBr + Br\bullet$

Which of these steps involve chain propagation?

A. I only

B. III only

C. I and II only

D. II and III only

E. I and III only

32. What statement(s) is/are true about an S_N2 reaction?

       I. A carbocation intermediate is formed

       II. The rate-determining step is bimolecular

       III. The mechanism has two steps

A. I only

B. II only

C. I and III only

D. II and III only

E. I, II and III

33. Which of the following compounds undergo(es) a substitution reaction?

       I. C_2H_6 II. C_2H_2 III. C_2H_4

A. I only

B. II only

C. I and II only

D. II and III only

E. I, II and III

34. Which of the following undergoes bimolecular nucleophilic substitution at the fastest rate?

A. 1-chloro-2,2-diethylcyclopentane

B. 1-chlorocyclopentane

C. 1-chlorocyclopentene

D. 1-chloro-1-ethylcyclopentane

E. *tert*-butylchloride

35. Which of the following is the best leaving group?

A. Cl^-

B. NH_2^-

C. ^-OH

D. Br^-

E. F^-

36. Which of the following is an example of the termination step for a free-radical chain reaction?

A. $Cl–Cl + h\nu \rightarrow 2\ Cl\cdot$

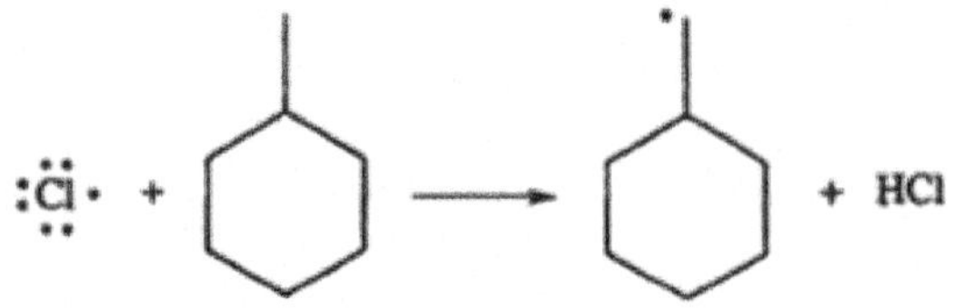

B.

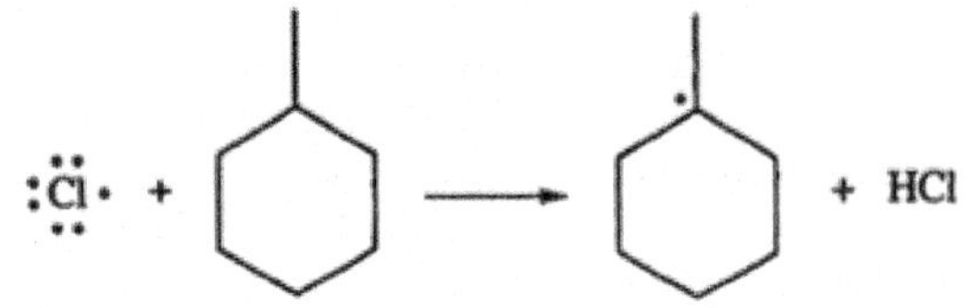

$$:\ddot{\underset{..}{Cl}}\cdot\ +\ \bigcirc\!\!-\!\!|\ \longrightarrow\ \bigcirc\!\!-\!\!|\ +\ HCl$$

C.

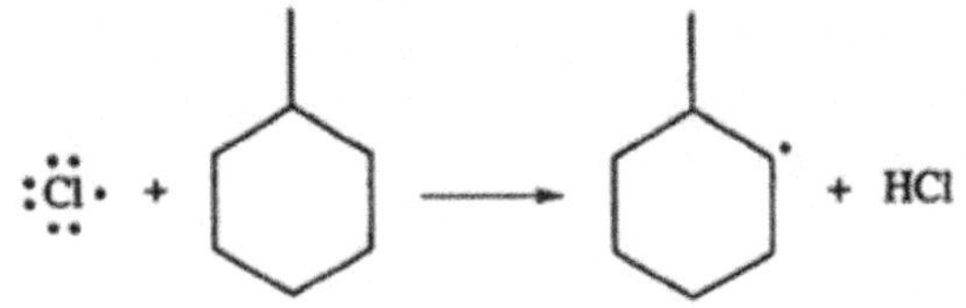

$$:\ddot{\underset{..}{Cl}}\cdot\ +\ \bigcirc\!\!-\!\!|\ \longrightarrow\ \bigcirc\!\!-\!\!|\ +\ HCl$$

D.

$$:\ddot{\underset{..}{Cl}}\cdot\ +\ \bigcirc\!\!-\!\!|\ \longrightarrow\ \bigcirc\!\!-\!\!|\ +\ HCl$$

E. $Cl\cdot + Cl\cdot \rightarrow Cl_2$

Notes for active learning

Notes for active learning

Alkenes

1. (*E*)- and (*Z*)-hex-3-ene can be subjected to a hydroboration-oxidation sequence. How are the products from these two reactions related?

    A. The products of the two isomers are diastereomers

    B. The products of the two isomers are constitutional isomers

    C. The (*E*)- and (*Z*)-isomers generate the same products in the same amounts

    D. The (*E*)- and (*Z*)-isomers generate the same products but in differing amounts

    E. The products of the two isomers are not structurally related

2. What is the major product of this reaction?

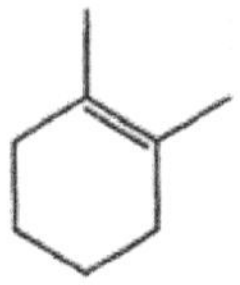

$+ D_2 / Pt \rightarrow ?$

A.

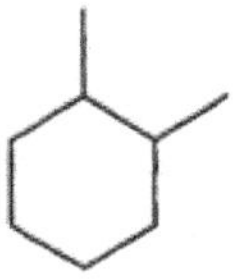

B.

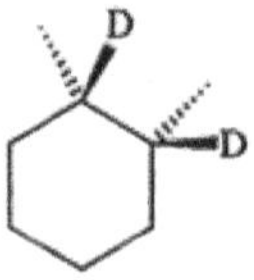

C.

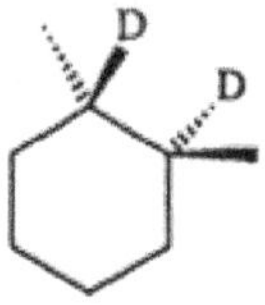

D.

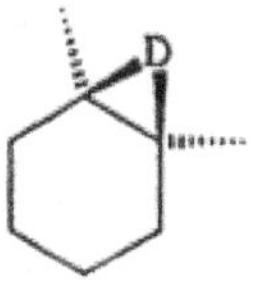

    E. None of the above

3. Give the best product for the following reaction:

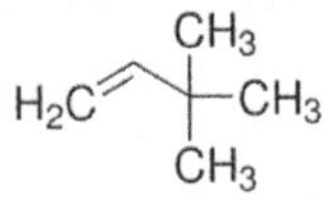

CH₃
H₂C⟍ ⫶—CH₃
       CH₃   + 1) Hg(O₂CCF₃)₂, CH₃CH₂OH; 2) NaBH₄ → ?

A.

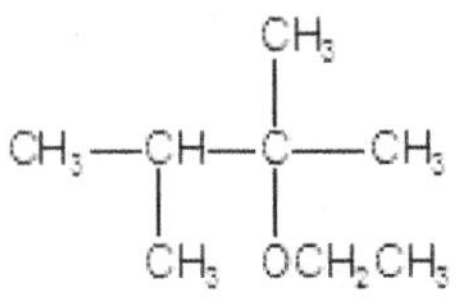

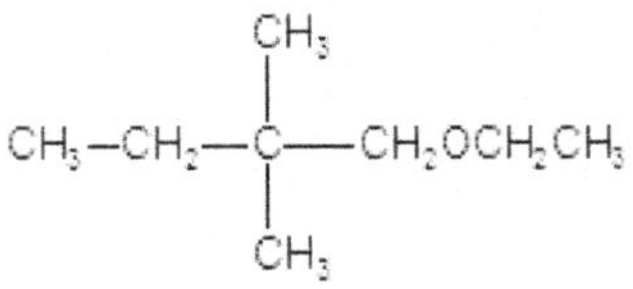

C.

B.

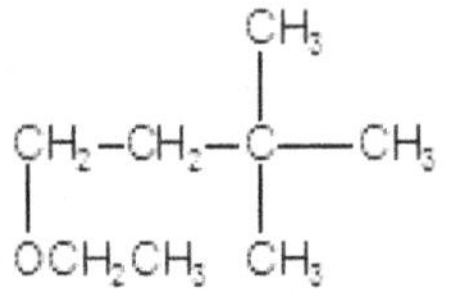

D.

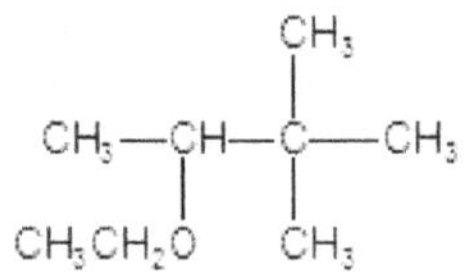

E.

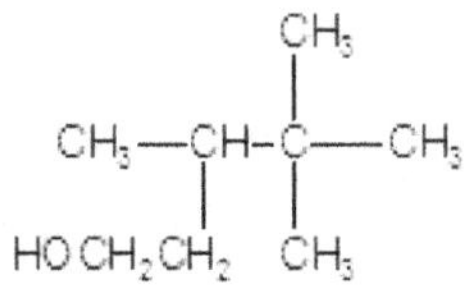

4. Which of the following correctly ranks the halides in order of increasing rate for addition to 3-hexene in a nonpolar aprotic solvent?

A. HI < HBr < HCl

B. HBr < HCl < HI

C. HCl < HI < HBr

D. HCl < HBr < HI

E. None of the above

5. The carbon–carbon single bond in 1,3-butadiene has a bond length that is shorter than a carbon–carbon single bond in an alkane. This is a result of:

A. overlap of two sp^3 orbitals

B. overlap of one sp^2 and one sp^3 orbital

C. partial double-bond character due to the σ electrons

D. overlap of two sp^2 orbitals

E. none of the above

6. What is the name of the major organic product of the following reaction?

$(CH_3)_2C=C(CH_3)_2 + H^+ / H_2O \rightarrow$?

A. 2,3-dimethyl-2-butanol

B. 2,3-dimethyl-1-butanol

C. 3,3-dimethyl-1-butanol

D. 3,3-dimethyl-2-butanol

E. 4-methyl-2-pentanol

7. The rate law for the addition of HBr to many simple alkenes may be approximated as rate = k[alkene]·[HBr]. This rate law indicates the following EXCEPT that the reaction:

A. occurs in a single step involving one HBr molecule and one alkene molecule

B. involves one HBr and one alkene molecule in the rate-determining step and may have many steps

C. is first order in HBr

D. is second order overall

E. is first order in the alkene

8. Which reactant is used to convert propene to 1,2-dichloropropane?

A. HCl

B. NaCl

C. H_2

D. Cl_2

E. BrCl

9. Using Zaitsev's rule, choose the most stable alkene among the following:

A. 1-methylcyclohexene

B. 3-methylcyclohexene

C. 4-methylcyclohexene

D. 3,4-dimethylcyclohexene

E. they are of equal stability

10. Which of the following has the lowest heat of hydrogenation per mole of H_2 absorbed?

A. 1,2-hexadiene

B. 1,3-hexadiene

C. 1,3,5-heptatriene

D. 1,5-hexadiene

E. 1,2,3-heptatriene

11. Which of the following is the best solvent for the addition of HCl to 3-hexene?

A. 3-hexene

B. CH_3CH_3

C. CH_3OH

D. H_2O

E. None of the above

12. What is the major product of the following reaction?

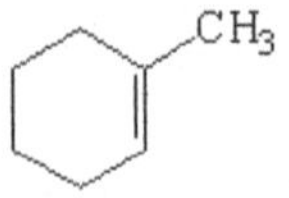

+ $H^+ / H_2O \rightarrow$?

A.

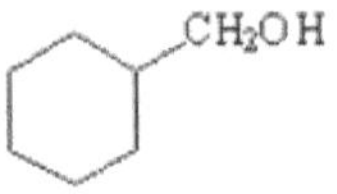

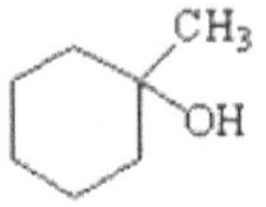

B.

C.

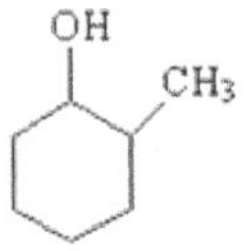

D.

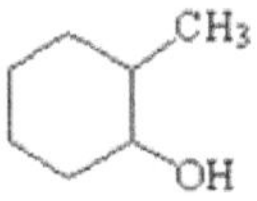

E.

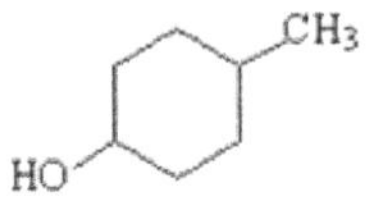

13. Which of the following is NOT an example of a conjugated system?

A. 1,2-butadiene

B. cyclobutadiene

C. benzene

D. 1,3-cyclohexadiene

E. 2,4-pentadiene

14. Which of the following would show the LEAST regioselectivity for HBr addition?

A. $(CH_3)_2C=C(CH_3)CH_2CH_3$

B. $H_2C=C(CH_3)CH_2CH_3$

C. $CH_2HC=C(CH_3)CH_2CH_3$

D. $(CH_3)_2C=CHCH_2CH_3$

E. $CH_2=CHCH_3$

15. Which statement is true in the oxymercuration-reduction of an alkene?

A. *Anti*-Markovnikov orientation and *anti*-addition occur

B. *Anti*-Markovnikov orientation and *syn*-addition occur

C. Markovnikov orientation and *anti*-addition occur

D. Markovnikov orientation and *syn*-addition occur

E. Zaitsev orientation and *anti*-addition occur

16. Which of the following compounds is/are geometric isomers?

        I. Isobutene

        II. (*E*)-2-butene

        III. *cis*-2-butene

        IV. *trans*-2-butene

  A. I and II only   **C.** III and IV only

  B. II and III only   **D.** II, III and IV only

                                      E. I, II, III and IV

17. Consider the following alcohol A.

The major product resulting from the dehydration of A is:

A.

B.

C.

D.

                           E. None of the above

18. What is the major product of the following reaction?

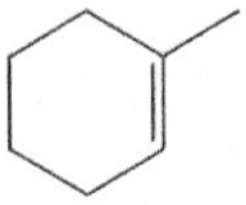

+ $Br_2 / H_2O \rightarrow$?

A.

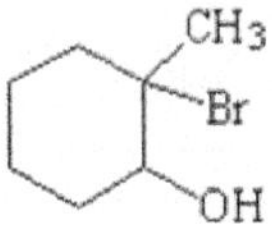

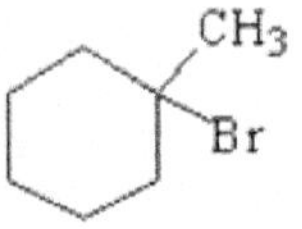

B.

C.

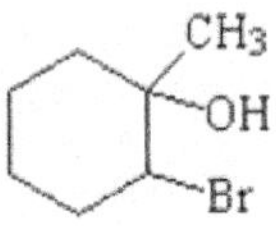

D.

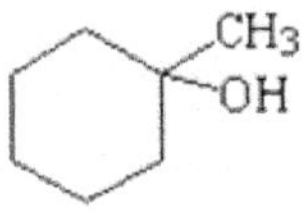

E.

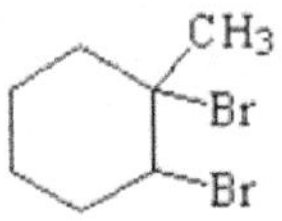

19. Which of the following reactions does NOT proceed through a bromonium ion intermediate?

A. $CH_3CH=CH_2 + Br_2 + H_2O \rightarrow CH_3CH_2OHCH_2Br + HBr$

B. $CH_2=CHCH_2CH_2CH=CH_2 + Br_2 \rightarrow CH_2BrCHBrCH_2CH_2CHBrCH_2Br$

C. $CH_3CH_2CH=CH_2 + Br_2 \rightarrow CH_3CH_2CHBrCH_2Br$

D. $CH_3CH_2CH=CH_2 + HBr \rightarrow CH_3CH_2CHBrCH_3$

E. None of the above

20. When reacted with HBr, *cis*-3-methyl-2-hexene most likely undergoes:

A. *anti*-Markovnikov *syn*- and *anti*-addition

B. *anti*-Markovnikov *syn*-addition

C. Markovnikov *syn*- and *anti*-addition

D. Markovnikov *syn*-addition

E. none of the above

21. The following are examples of addition reactions of alkenes, EXCEPT:

A. hydrogenation

B. hydration

C. oxidation

D. bromination

E. ozonolysis

22. Which of the following reactions will NOT occur?

   Reaction 1: butene + NBS → 2-bromobutane

   Reaction 2: 2-methylbutane + 8 O_2 + heat → 5 CO_2 + 6 H_2O

   Reaction 3: 2-methylbutane + Br_2 + hv → 2-bromo-2-methylbutane

   Reaction 4: 2-methyl-2-butene + Br_2 + CCl_4 → 2,3-dibromo-2-methylbutane (+ enantiomer)

   A. Reaction 1   **C.** Reaction 3
   B. Reaction 2   **D.** Reaction 4
                                         E. Reactions 2 and 4

23. Give the possibilities in the structure for a compound with a formula of C_6H_{10}:

   A. no rings; no double bonds; no triple bonds

   B. one double bond; or one ring

   C. two rings; two double bonds; one double bond and one ring; or one triple bond

   D. three rings; three double bonds; two double bonds and one ring; one ring and two double bonds; one triple bond and one ring; or one double bond and one ring

   E. benzene

24. Which of the following is/are the most stable diene?

A.

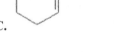

C.

B.

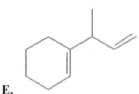

D.

E.

25. Products A, B, and C of the following reaction are, respectively:

2-methyl-2-butene + HBr   →   product A

2-methyl-2-butene + HBr / H_2O_2 →   product B

2-methyl-2-butene + H_2O / H^+ / heat →   product C

Product A	Product B	Product C
A. 2-bromo-2-methylbutane	2-bromo-3-methylbutane	2-methyl-2-butanol
B. 3-methyl-2-bromobutene	3-methyl-2-bromobutane	2-methyl-2-butanol
C. 2-bromo-2-methylbutane	2-bromo-2-methylbutane	3-methyl-2-butanol
D. 1-bromo-2-methyl-2-butene	2-bromo-2-methylbutane	2-methyl-2-butane
E. None of the above		

26. Which of the following is vinyl chloride?

A. CH_2=CHCl

C.

B. CH_2=CHCH$_2$Cl

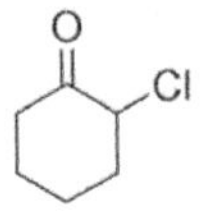

D.

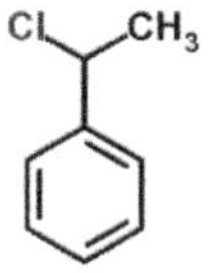

E. CH_3CH_2Cl

27. What reagent(s) is/are needed to accomplish the following transformation?

A. BH_3 / THF

B. $^-$OH

C. H_2O / H_2O_2

D. H_2O / H^+

E. 1) BH_3 / THF; 2) $^-$OH, H_2O_2, H_2O

28. The reaction below can be classified as a(n):

cis-pent-2-ene → pentane

A. tautomerization

B. elimination

C. oxidation

D. reduction

E. substitution

29. The major product of the following reaction will likely be the result of a(n) [   ] mechanism?

       2-bromobutane + *tert*-butyl alkoxide

A. E_2

B. E_1

C. S_N2

D. S_N1

E. S_N1 and E_1

30. What is the major product from the following reaction?

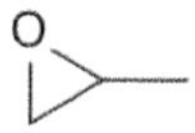

+ HBr → ?

A.  —CH₂Br

B.

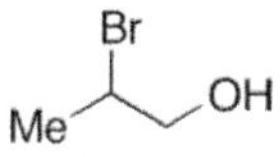

C.

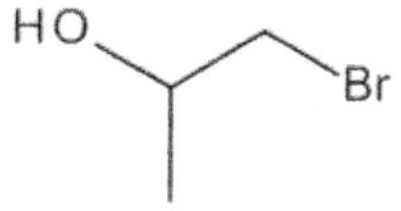

D.

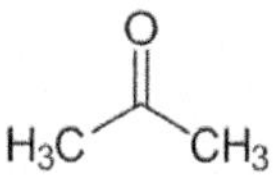

E.

31. When CH_3–CH=CH_2 is reacted in water with a catalytic amount of acid, a new compound is formed. What might be the product of this reaction?

A.

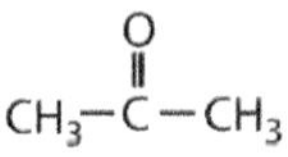

B.

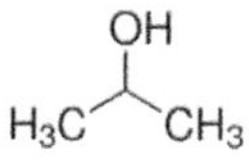

C.

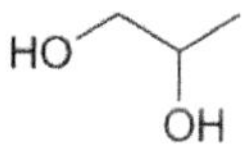

D. CH_3–CH–CH_2

E.

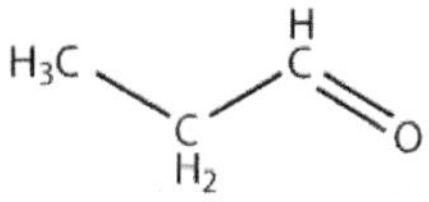

32. What is the product of the following reaction?

     + H₂SO₄/Δ → ?

A.

B.

C.

D.

E.

33. Alkenes are more acidic than alkanes. What is the best explanation of this property?

A. The sp^2 hybridized orbitals in alkenes stabilize the negative charge generated when a proton is abstracted

B. The sp^2 hybridized orbitals in alkenes destabilize the negative charge generated when a proton is abstracted

C. The sp^3 hybridized orbitals in alkenes stabilize the negative charge generated when a proton is abstracted

D. The sp^3 hybridized orbitals in alkenes destabilize the negative charge generated when a proton is abstracted

E. The alkene is small and less sterically hindered compared to the alkane.

34. What is the major product formed from the reaction of 2-bromo-2-methylpentane with sodium ethoxide?

A. 2-methylpent-2-ene

B. 2-methylpent-3-ene

C. 2-methyl-2-methoxypentane

D. 2-methylpentene

E. 1-methylpentene

35. What reagents can best be used to accomplish the following transformation?

A. 1) Hg(OAc)₂, H₂O / THF; 2) NaBH₄

B. 1) Hg(O₂CCF₃)₂, CH₃OH; 2) NaBH₄

C. 1) BH₃·THF; 2) HO⁻, H₂O₂

D. H⁺, H₂O

E. NaOH, H₂O

36. Heating a(n) [ ] results in a Cope elimination.

A. amine oxide

B. imine

C. enamine

D. oxime

E. enol

Notes for active learning

Notes for active learning

Alkynes

1. What is the major organic product when 3-heptyne is subjected to excess hydrogen and a platinum catalyst?

A. (*E*)-3-heptene

B. (*Z*)-3-heptene

C. (*Z*)-2-heptene

D. 2-heptyne

E. heptane

2. In the addition of hydrogen bromide to alkynes in the absence of peroxides, which of the following species is proposed as an intermediate?

A. carbene

B. vinyl radical

C. vinyl cation

D. vinyl anion

E. none of the above

3. Which of the following molecular formulas correspond(s) to an acyclic alkyne?

I. C_9H_{20} II. C_9H_{18} III. C_9H_{16}

A. I only

B. II only

C. III only

D. I and II only

E. I, II and III

4. What is the term for a family of unsaturated hydrocarbon compounds with a triple bond?

A. alkynes

B. arenes

C. alkanes

D. alkenes

E. none of the above

5. Which of the following molecular formulas correspond(s) to an alkyne?

I. $C_{10}H_{18}$ II. $C_{10}H_{20}$ III. $C_{10}H_{22}$

A. I only

B. II only

C. III only

D. I and II only

E. I, II and III

6. What is the product from the reaction of one mole of acetylene and two moles of hydrogen gas using a platinum catalyst?

A. propene

B. propane

C. ethene

D. ethane

E. none of the above

7. Which of the following does NOT accurately describe the physical properties of an alkyne?

  A. Less dense than water

  B. Insoluble in most organic solvents

  C. Relatively nonpolar

  D. Nearly insoluble in water

  E. Boiling point nearly the same as an alkane with a similar carbon skeleton

8. What are the two products from the complete combustion of an alkyne?

  A. CO_2 and H_2O

  B. CO_2 and H_2

  C. CO and H_2O

  D. CO and H_2

  E. None of the above

9. The compound propyne consists of how many carbon atoms and how many hydrogen atoms?

  A. 3C,2H

  B. 3C,6H

  C. 3C,4H

  D. 2C,2H

  E. None of the above

10. Given that 1-butyne has a boiling point of 8.1 °C, what is the phase of propyne at room temperature and 1 atm pressure?

  A. solid

  B. supercritical fluid

  C. gas

  D. liquid

  E. vapor

11. How many moles of hydrogen are required to convert a mole of pentyne to pentane?

  A. 0

  B. 1

  C. 2

  D. 3

  E. 4

12. What is the product of the reaction of one mole of acetylene and one mole of bromine vapor?

  A. 1,1,2,2-tetrabromoethane

  B. 1,1,2,2-tetrabromoethene

  C. 1,2-dibromoethane

  D. 1,2-dibromoethene

  E. None of the above

13. What reagents are used to convert 1-hexyne into 2-hexanone?

  A. 1) Si_2BH; 2) H_2O_2, NaOH

  B. Hg^{2+}, H_2SO_4, H_2O

  C. 1) O_3; 2) $(CH_3)_2S$

  D. 1) CH_3MgBr; 2) CO_2

  E. 1) H_2, Ni; 2) $Na_2Cr_2O_7$, H_2SO_4

14. What is the major product of this reaction?

$$H_3C–C≡C–CH_3 + Na\ (s),\ NH_3\ (l) → ?$$

A.

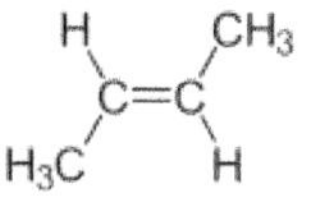

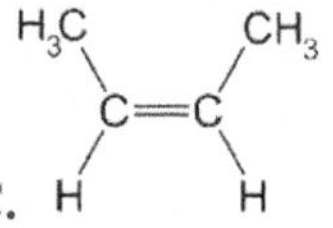

B.

C.

D.

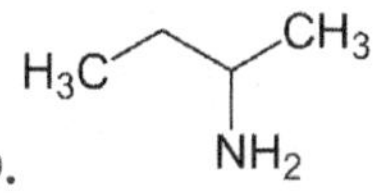

E.

15. What is the major product of the following acid/catalyzed hydration reaction?

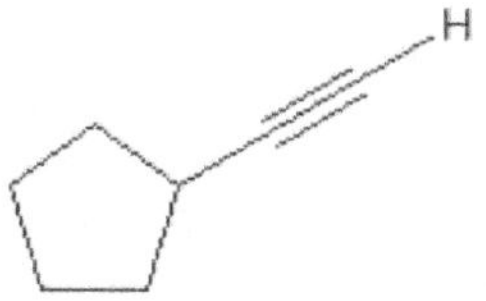

$$+ H_2O / H_2SO_4,\ HgSO_4 → ?$$

A.

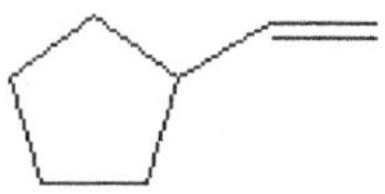

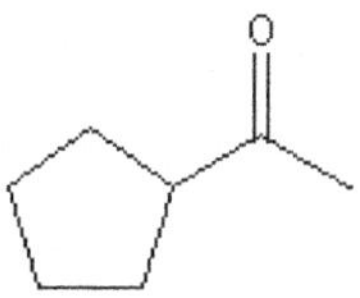

B.

C.

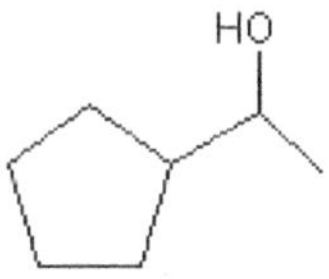

D.

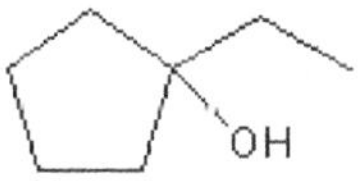

E.

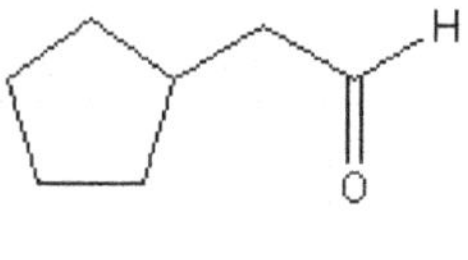

16. When 2,2-dibromobutane is heated to 200 °C with molten KOH, what is the major organic product?

A. but-1-yne

B. but-2-yne

C. 1-bromobut-1-yne

D. 1-bromobut-2-yne

E. but-1-ene

17. What class of organic product results when 1-heptyne is treated with a mixture of mercuric acetate [Hg(OAc)$_2$] in aqueous sulfuric acid (H$_2$SO$_4$), followed by sodium borohydride (NaBH$_4$)?

A. diol

B. ketone

C. aldehyde

D. alcohol

E. carboxylic acid

18. Which of the following describes the reaction below?

$$H_3C \text{—}\!\!\equiv\!\!\text{—} CH_3 + H_2, Pd, CaCo_3, \text{quinolone, hexane} \rightarrow$$

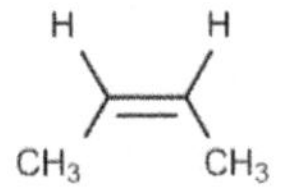

A. oxidation

B. reduction

C. substitution

D. catalytic hydration

E. elimination

19. What is the general molecular formula for the alkyne class of compounds?

I. C$_n$H$_{2n+2}$ II. C$_n$H$_{2n}$ III. C$_n$H$_{2n-2}$

A. I only

B. II only

C. III only

D. II and III only

E. I, II and III

20. Among the following compounds, which acids are stronger than ammonia?

I. water   II. ethane   III. butyne   IV. but-2-yne

A. I and II only

B. II only

C. I and III only

D. II and III only

E. I, II, III and IV

21. In reducing alkynes using sodium in liquid ammonia, which of the species below is NOT an intermediate in the commonly accepted mechanism?

A. vinyl anion

B. vinyl cation

C. anion

D. vinyl radical

E. all are intermediates

22. For isomers with the formula C$_{10}$H$_{16}$, which of the following structural features are NOT possible?

A. 2 rings and 1 double bond

B. 2 double bonds and 1 ring

C. 2 triple bonds

D. 1 ring and 1 triple bond

E. 3 double bonds

23. What is the product from the reaction of one mole of acetylene and one mole of hydrogen gas using a platinum catalyst?

A. propane

B. propene

C. ethane

D. ethene

E. 2-butene

24. Which of the species below is less basic than an acetylide?

    I. CH_3Li II. CH_3MgBr III. CH_3ONa

A. I only

B. II only

C. III only

D. I and II only

E. I, II and III

25. Which is the most stable product for the reaction below:

+ 1) BH_3 / THF; 2) ^-OH, H_2O_2, H_2O

A.

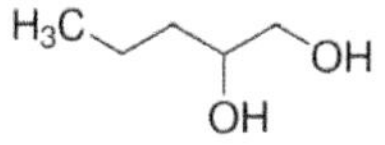

B. $CH_3CH_2CH_2CH=CHOH$

C.

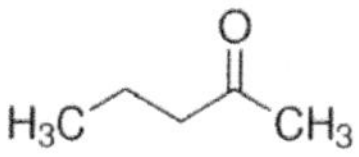

D.

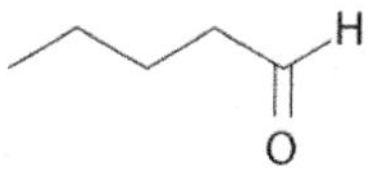

E. $CH_3CH_2CH_2(OH)C=CH_2$

26. The compound 1-butyne contains:

A. a ring structure

B. a triple bond

C. a double bond

D. all single bonds

E. a bromine atom

27. The *pi* bond of an alkyne is [ ] and [ ] than the *pi* bond of an alkene.

A. longer; stronger

B. longer; weaker

C. shorter; stronger

D. shorter; weaker

E. none of the above

28. What is the major product of this reaction?

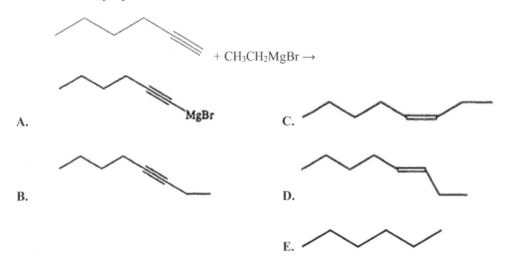

+ $CH_3CH_2MgBr \rightarrow$

A. MgBr

B.

C.

D.

E.

29. Which of the following is the product for the reaction?

$HC \equiv C$ ... CH_3 + H_2O + $HgSO_4 / H_2SO_4 \rightarrow$

A. $CH_3CH_2CH_2C{=}CH_2$ with OH

B. $CH_3CH_2CH_2CH{=}CHOH$

C. H_3C ... CH_3 with O

D. $CH_3CH_2CH_2CH_2CHO$

E. $CH_3CH_2CH_2CH(OH)CH_2OH$

30. What is the product from the reaction of one mole of acetylene and two moles of bromine vapor?

A. 1,1,2,2-tetrabromoethene

B. 1,1,2,2-tetrabromoethane

C. 1,2-dibromoethene

D. 1,2-dibromoethane

E. none of the above

31. Which of the alkyne addition reactions below involve(s) an enol intermediate?

   I. hydroboration/oxidation

   II. treatment with $HgSO_4$ in dilute H_2SO_4

   III. hydrogenation

A. I only

B. II only

C. III only

D. I and II only

E. I and III only

32. Which of the following is the final and major product of this reaction?

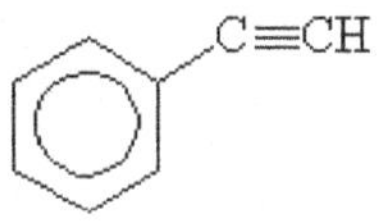

+ H_2O, $H_2SO_4/HgSO_4 \rightarrow$?

A.

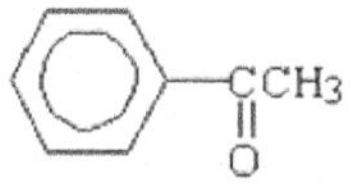

C.

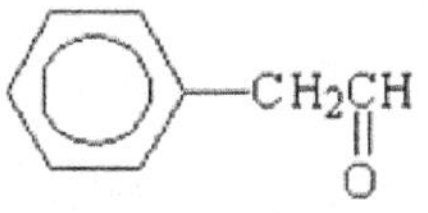

B.

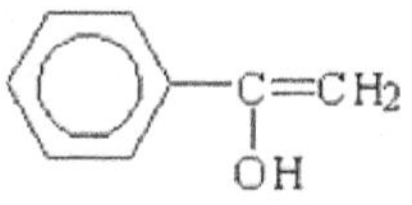

D.

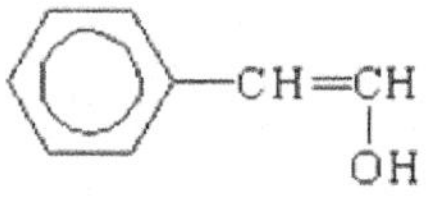

E.

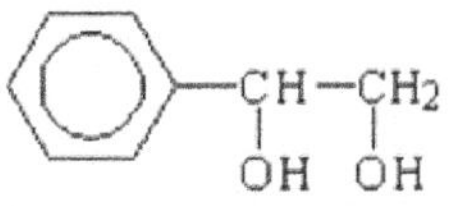

33. If the compound C_5H_7NO contains 1 ring, how many *pi* bonds are there in this compound?

A. 0   **C.** 2
B. 1   **D.** 3
                          E. 4

34. Which of the following is the major product of this reaction?

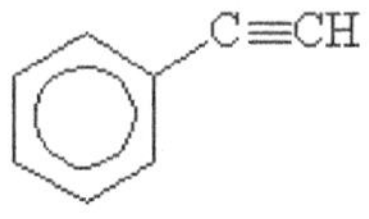

+ 1) BH_3, THF + 2) ^-OH, H_2O_2, $H_2O \rightarrow$

A.

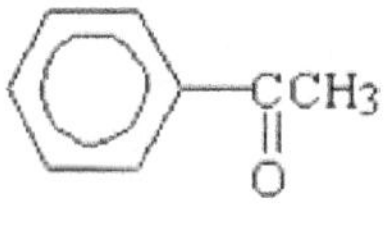

C.

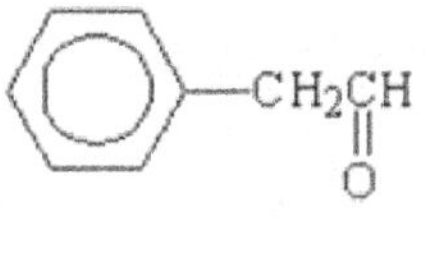

B.

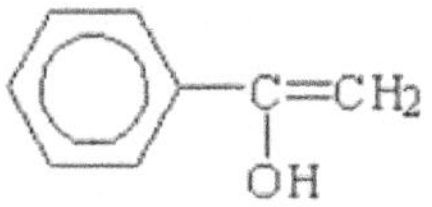

D.

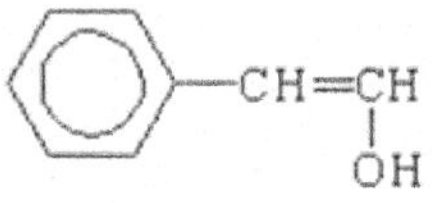

E.

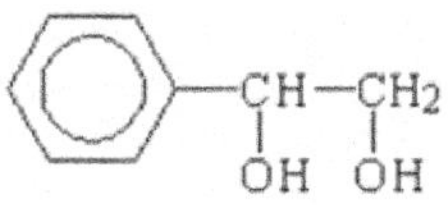

35. Which of the following statements correctly describes the general reactivity of alkynes?

A. Unlike alkenes, alkynes fail to undergo electrophilic addition reactions

B. Alkynes are generally more reactive than alkenes

C. An alkyne is an electron-rich molecule and therefore reacts as a nucleophile

D. The σ bonds of alkynes are higher in energy than the π bonds, and thus are more reactive

E. Alkynes react as electrophiles, whereas alkenes react as nucleophiles

36. What is the major product when C_2H_4 undergoes an addition reaction with 1 mole equivalent of Br_2 in CCl_4?

A. $C_2H_2 + H_2$

B. $C_2H_4Br_2$

C. $C_2HBr + HBr$

D. C_2H_3Br

E. None of the above

Notes for active learning

Notes for active learning

Aromatic Compounds

1. What is the major product of this reaction?

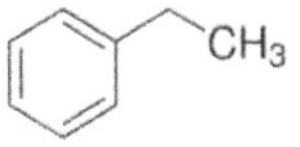

$+ C(CH_3)_3Br + FeBr \rightarrow$?

A.

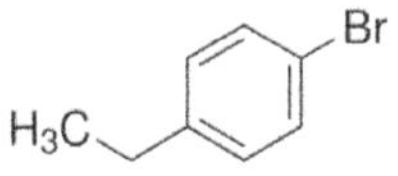

B.

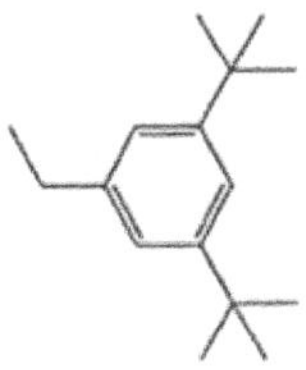

C.

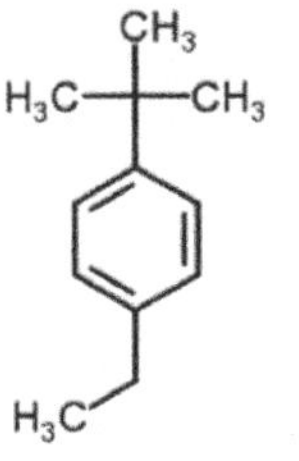

D.

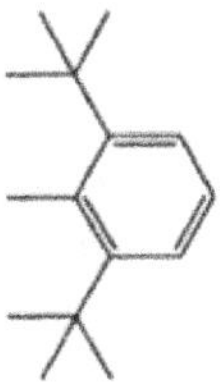

E.

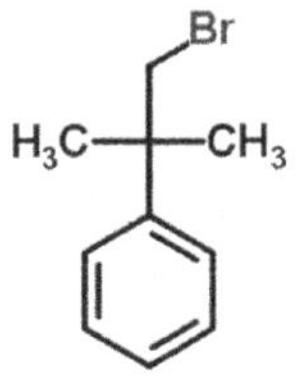

2. The following are common reactions of benzene, EXCEPT:

A. nitration

B. hydrogenation

C. chlorination

D. bromination

E. sulfonation

3. How many pairs of degenerate π molecular orbitals are in benzene?

A. 6

B. 5

C. 4

D. 3

E. 2

4. What is the effect of an ammonium substituent on electrophilic aromatic substitution?

    A. *ortho/para*-directing with activation
    B. *ortho/para*-directing with deactivation

    C. *meta*-directing with activation
    D. *meta*-directing with deactivation
    E. neither directing nor activating

5. Which of the following compounds undergoes Friedel-Crafts alkylation with $(CH_3)_3CCl$, $AlCl_3$ most rapidly?

    A. toluene
    B. iodobenzene

    C. acetophenone
    D. benzenesulfonic acid
    E. cyanobenzene

6. Which sequence correctly ranks the following aromatic rings in order of increasing rate of reactivity in an electrophilic aromatic substitution reaction?

      I.   II.   III.

    A. II < I < III
    B. II < III < I

    C. III < I < II
    D. I < II < III
    E. I < III < II

7. Of the following, which reacts most readily with $Br_2/FeBr_3$ in an electrophilic aromatic substitution?

    A.

    B.

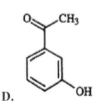

    C.

    D.

    E. The compounds have the same reactivity

8. In the molecular orbital representation of benzene, how many π molecular orbitals are present?

    A. 1
    B. 2

    C. 4
    D. 6
    E. 8

9. Which of the following structures is aromatic?

A.

B.

C.

D.

E.

10. In the electrophilic aromatic substitution of phenol, substituents add predominantly in which position(s)?

    I. *ortho* to the hydroxyl group

    II. *meta* to the hydroxyl group

    III. *para* to the hydroxyl group

A. I only

B. II only

C. III only

D. I and III only

E. I, II and III

11. Which of the following is NOT aromatic?

A.

B.

C.

D.

E. All of the above

12. Which of these molecules is aromatic?

A.

B.

C.

D.

E. None of the above

13. What is the most likely regiochemistry of this electrophilic aromatic substitution reaction?

+ Br₂ / FeBr₃ → ?

A.

B.

C.

D.

E.

14. A compound is a six-carbon cyclic hydrocarbon. It is inert to bromine in water and bromine in dichloromethane, yet it decolorizes bromine in carbon tetrachloride when a small quantity of FeBr₃ is added. Which of the following is the identity of the compound?

    A. 1,4-cyclohexadiene   **C.** benzene

    B. 1,3-cyclohexadiene   **D.** cyclohexane

                                     E. cyclohexyne

15. While electron-withdrawing groups (such as $\sim NO_2$ and $\sim CO_2R$) are *meta*-directing with regard to electrophilic aromatic substitution reactions, they are *ortho-* / *para*-directing in nucleophilic aromatic substitution reactions. This observation would best be explained by using which concept?

A. tautomerism

B. aromaticity

C. hydrogen bonding

D. resonance

E. equilibration

16. Derivatives of the compound shown below are currently being examined for their effectiveness in treating drug addiction and metabolic syndrome. Which sequence ranks the aromatic rings of this compound in order of increasing reactivity (slowest to fastest reacting) in an electrophilic aromatic substitution reaction?

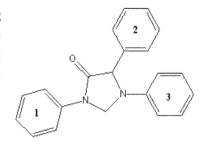

A. $1 < 2 < 3$

B. $2 < 3 < 1$

C. $3 < 2 < 1$

D. $3 < 1 < 2$

E. $2 < 1 < 3$

17. The major aromatic product of the following reaction is:

A. methyl ketone substitutes in the *ortho* / *para* position

B. methyl ketone substitutes in the *meta* position

C. methyl ketone replacing the bromine

D. formation of phenol

E. formation of benzene

18. In electrophilic aromatic substitution reactions, an extremely reactive electrophile is typically used because the aromatic ring is:

A. a poor electrophile

B. nonpolar

C. reactive

D. a poor nucleophile

E. unstable

19. What is the effect of each of $\sim Cl$ substituents on electrophilic aromatic substitution?

A. *meta*-directing with deactivation

B. *meta*-directing with activation

C. *ortho/para*-directing with deactivation

D. *ortho*-directing with activation

E. *para*-directing with activation

20. 1,3-cyclopentadiene reacts with sodium metal at low temperatures according to:

What is the best explanation for this observation?

    A. Rehybridization of the saturated carbon atoms provides additional product stability

    B. Sodium metal is highly selective for cycloalkenes

    C. Aromaticity stabilizes the carbocation

    D. The reactant is more unstable at reduced temperatures

    E. Aromaticity stabilizes the anion

21. What is the major product of this electrophile aromatic substitution (EAS) reaction?

$$+ \, HNO_3 \, / \, H_2SO_4 \rightarrow \, ?$$

    A.

    C.

    B.

    D.

    E.

22. Which of the following molecules reacts the slowest in electrophilic nitration?

A. Toluene

B. Aniline

C. Anisole (methoxybenzene)

D. Bromobenzene

E. Phenol

23. In electrophilic aromatic substitution, the aromatic ring acts as a(n):

A. leaving group

B. dienophile

C. nucleophile

D. electrophile

E. spectator

24. What is the effect of ~F substituents on electrophilic aromatic substitution?

A. *meta*-directing with activation

B. *meta*-directing with deactivation

C. *ortho*- / *para*-directing with activation

D. *ortho*- / *para*-directing with deactivation

E. *ortho*-directing with activation

25. Which of the following compounds is least susceptible to electrophilic aromatic substitution?

A. p-H_3CCH_2O–C_6H_4–O–CH_2CH_3

B. p-O_2N–C_6H_4–NH–CH_3

C. p-Cl–C_6H_4–NH_3^+

D. p-CH_3CH_2–C_6H_4–CH_2CH_3

E. benzene

26. Which of the following statements is NOT correct about benzene?

A. The carbon-carbon bond lengths are the same

B. The carbon-hydrogen bond lengths are the same

C. All of the carbon atoms are *sp* hybridized

D. It has delocalized electrons

E. All twelve atoms lie in the same plane

27. Which reaction is NOT characteristic of aromatic compounds?

A. addition

B. halogenation

C. nitration

D. sulfonation

E. acylation

28. The reason why complete hydrogenation of benzene to cyclohexane requires H_2, rhodium (Rh) catalyst, and 1,000 psi pressure at 100 °C is because:

    A. the double bonds in benzene have the same reactivity as *pi* bonds of non-aromatic alkenes

    B. hydrogenation produces an aromatic compound

    C. the double bonds in benzene are more reactive than a typical alkene

    D. the double bonds in benzene are less reactive than a typical alkene

    E. none of the above

29. Which of the following reactions is NOT an electrophilic aromatic substitution reaction?

    A. $CH_3C_6H_5 + C_6H_5CH_2CH_2Cl / AlCl_3$

    B. $CH_3C_6H_5 + Br_2 / FeBr_3$

    C. $CH_3C_6H_5 + CH_3CH_2CH_2COCl / AlCl_3$

    D. $CH_3C_6H_5 + H_2, Rh / C$

    E. $C_6H_6 + HSO_3 / H_2SO_4$

30. Which steps may be used to synthesize 1-chloro-4-nitrobenzene, starting from benzene?

    A. 1) Na / NH_3; 2) $Cl_2 / FeCl_3$

    B. 1) HNO_3 / H_2SO_4; 2) $Cl_2 / FeCl_3$

    C. 1) HCl / H_2O; 2) HNO_3 / H_2SO_4

    D. 1) $Cl_2 / FeCl_3$; 2) HNO_3 / H_2SO_4

    E. Cl_2 / CCl_4

31. If bromobenzene is treated with sulfur trioxide (SO_3) and concentrated H_2SO_4, what is/are the major product(s)?

    A. *ortho*- and *para*-bromobenzenesulfonic acid

    B. benzene

    C. benzenesulfonic acid

    D. *meta*-bromobenzenesulfonic acid

    E. toluene

32. Rank the following three molecules in increasing order according to the rate they react with $Br_2/FeBr_3$.

I.   II.   III.

    A. II < III < I

    B. II < I < III

    C. I < II < III

    D. I < III < II

    E. III < II < I

33. Which of the following is true about the benzene molecule?

    A. It is a saturated hydrocarbon

    B. The *pi* electrons of the ring move around the ring and have resonance

    C. It is a hydrocarbon with the molecular formula of C_nH_{2n+2}

    D. It contains heterocyclic oxygen

    E. Attachments to the ring can exhibit *cis/trans* isomerism

34. Which of the following statements is supported by the table below?

	Solubility (g/L H_2O)	Melting point (°C)
para-nitrophenol	10	112
meta-nitrophenol	2.7	98
ortho-nitrophenol	0.8	47

    A. *Meta*- and *para*-nitrophenol form intramolecular hydrogen bonds

    B. *Ortho*-nitrophenol does not form intermolecular hydrogen bonds

    C. *Ortho*-nitrophenol has the greatest intramolecular hydrogen bonding

    D. *Para*-nitrophenol has the weakest intermolecular hydrogen bonding

    E. *Ortho*-nitrophenol has the weakest intramolecular hydrogen bonding

35. Which of the molecules shown below is NOT an *aromatic* compound?

    A. 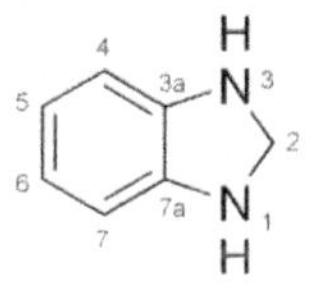 Benzimidazoline

    B.  Thiophene

    C. 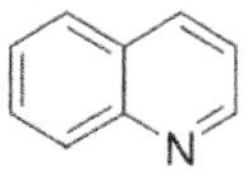 Quinoline

    D. 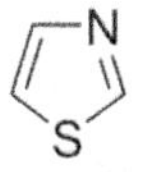 Thiazole

    E. 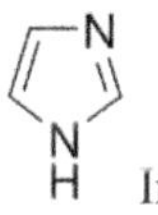 Imidazole

36. What is the degree of unsaturation for benzene?

    A. 1   **C.** 3

    B. 2   **D.** 4

                    E. 5

Notes for active learning

Alcohols

1. Which of the following alcohols has the highest boiling point?

   A. 2-methyl-1-propanol

   B. hexanol

   C. ethanol

   D. propanol

   E. methanol

2. When phenol acts as an acid, a [   ] ion is produced.

   A. phenolic acid

   B. benzol

   C. phenyl

   D. benzyl

   E. phenoxide

3. When alcohol reacts with phosphoric acid, the product is a:

   A. pyrophosphate

   B. phosphate anion

   C. phosphate ester

   D. phosphate salt

   E. none of the above

4. Which formula is alcohol?

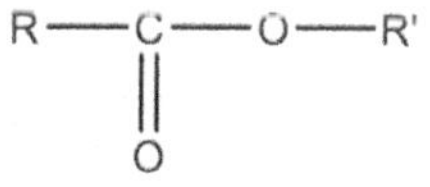

   A. 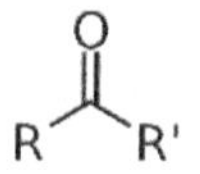
   $$R \overset{O}{\underset{}{\overset{\|}{C}}} R'$$

   B.
   $$R - \overset{}{\underset{O}{\overset{\|}{C}}} - O - R'$$

   C.
   $$R - \overset{}{\underset{O}{\overset{\|}{C}}} - O - H$$

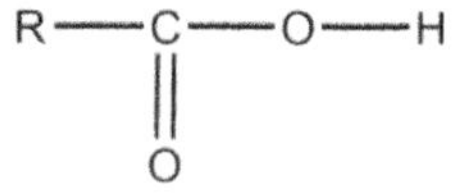

   D. 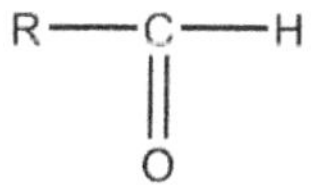
   $$R - \overset{}{\underset{O}{\overset{\|}{C}}} - H$$

   E. R—O—H

5. The alcohol and carboxylic acid required to form propyl ethanoate are [   ] and [   ]:

   A. 1-propanol ... ethanoic acid

   B. propanol ... propanoic acid

   C. ethanol ... propionic acid

   D. methanol ... propionic acid

   E. 2-propanol ... ethanoic acid

6. Which compound has the highest boiling point?

A. $CH_3CH_2CH_2CH_2OH$

B. $CH_3CH_2CH_2CH_3$

C. $CH_3CH_2CH_2CH_2CH_2OH$

D. $CH_3CH_2CH_2CH_2CH_3$

E. $CH_3CH_2CH_2OH$

7. The functional group, ~OH, is in which of these types of organic compounds?

A. amines

B. alcohols

C. alkanes

D. alkenes

E. ethers

8. What is the major product of this reaction?

Ph—CH₂—CH₂—OH + $Na_2Cr_2O_7 / H_2SO_4 \rightarrow$?

A. Ph / CH₂ (with H)

C. Ph—CH₂—CHO

B. Ph—CH₂—CH₂—OSO₃H

D. Ph—CH₂—C(=O)—OH

E. None of the above

9. Which of the following reagents is best to convert methyl alcohol to methyl chloride?

A. Cl^-

B. $SOCl_2$

C. Cl_2/CCl_4

D. Cl_2/hv

E. NaCl

10. The compound below has which functional groups?

A. ether, alkene and alcohol

B. ester, alkene and alcohol

C. aromatic, alcohol and ether

D. aromatic, alcohol and ester

E. ether and ester

11. Which compound is NOT an unsaturated compound?

A. $H_2C=CH-Cl$

B. CH_3-CH_2-O-H

C. $H_2C=CH_2$

D. $CH_3-CH=CH_2$

E. $H_2C=CH-O-H$

12. Compounds of the type R_3C-OH are referred to as [   ] alcohols.

A. primary

B. secondary

C. tertiary

D. quaternary

E. none of the above

13. Compounds with the ~OH group attached to a saturated alkane-like carbon are:

A. ethers

B. hydroxyls

C. alcohols

D. alkyl halides

E. phenols

14. When (S)-2-heptanol is subjected to $SOCl_2$/pyridine, the compound is transformed into:

A. (R/S)-2-chloroheptane

B. (R)-2-chloroheptane

C. (S)-2-chloroheptane

D. 2-heptone

E. heptanoic acid

15. The ester prepared by heating 1-pentanol with acetic acid in the presence of an acidic catalyst is:

A. 1-pentyl acetate

B. acetyl 1-pentanoate

C. acetic pentanoate

D. pentanoic acetate

E. acetyl pentanol

16. Which of the following has the highest boiling point?

A. ethyl methyl ether

B. dihexyl ether

C. dimethyl ether

D. diethyl ether

E. dipropyl ether

17. Based on the properties of the attached functional group, which compound interacts most strongly with water, thus making it the most soluble compound?

A. CH_3-CH_2-S-H

B. CH_3-CH_2-I

C. CH_3-CH_2-F

D. CH_3-CH_2-Cl

E. CH_3-CH_2-O-H

18. What is the product of the following reaction?

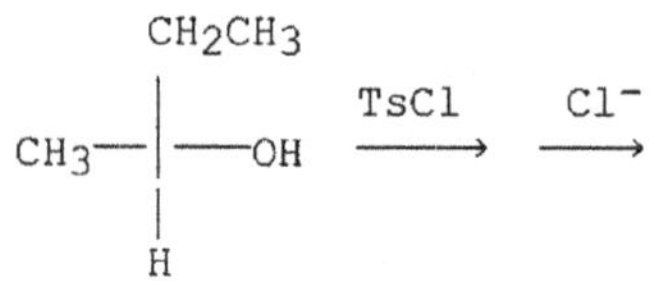

CH₃—C(CH₂CH₃)(H)—OH →(TsCl) →(Cl⁻)

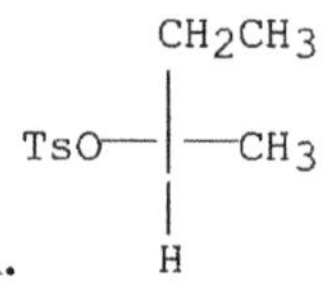

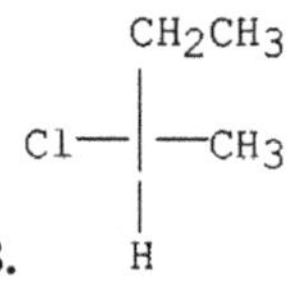

A. TsO—C(CH₂CH₃)(H)—CH₃

C. CH₃—C(CH₂CH₃)(H)—OTs

B. Cl—C(CH₂CH₃)(H)—CH₃

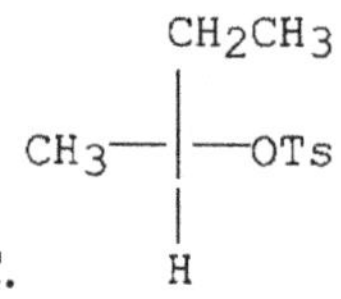

D. CH₃—C(CH₂CH₃)(H)—Cl

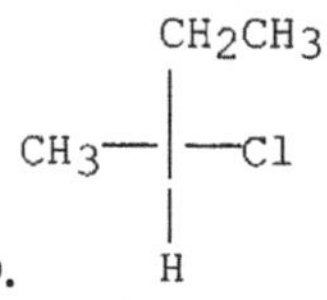

E. CH₃—C(CH₂CH₃)(H)—OCl

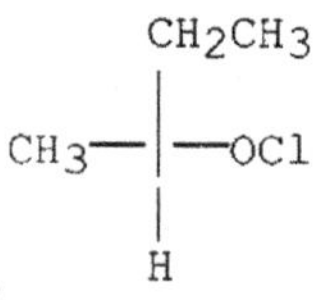

19. Which of the following alcohols has the lowest boiling point?

A. hexanol

B. 2-methyl-1-propanol

C. propanol

D. ethanol

E. benzoic acid

20. The reaction of $(CH_3)_2CHCH_2OH$ with concentrated HBr using controlled heating yields:

A. $(CH_3)_2CHCH_2OBr$

B. $(CH_3)_2CHCH_4^+Br^-$

C. $CH_3CH_2CH_2Br$

D. $(CH_3)_2CHCH_2Br$

E. $(CH_3)_2CHCH_3$

21. When propanol is subjected to PBr_3, the compounds undergo:

A. an S_N1 elimination reaction to form propene

B. oxidation to form an aldehyde

C. an S_N1 reaction to produce an alkyl halide

D. addition, elimination, and then substitution to form bromopropane

E. an E_1 reaction to produce propene

22. Which is a product of the oxidation of CH_3–CH_2–CH_2–O–H?

A. CH_3–CH_2–CH_3

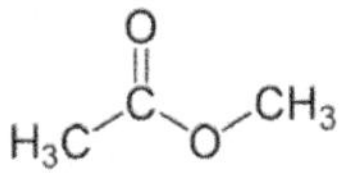

C.

B.

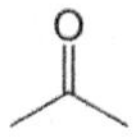

D.

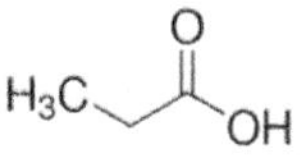

E. CH_3–CH_2–O–CH_3

23. Which of the following has the highest boiling point?

A.

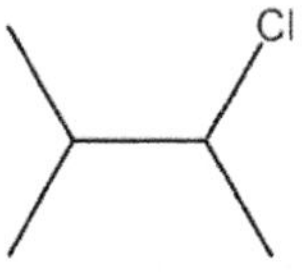

B.

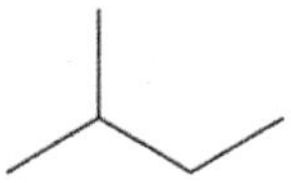

C.

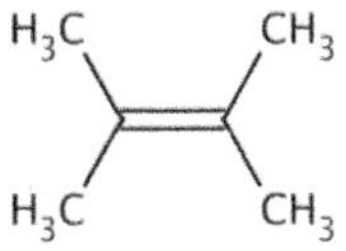

D.

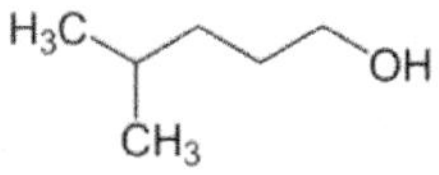

E.

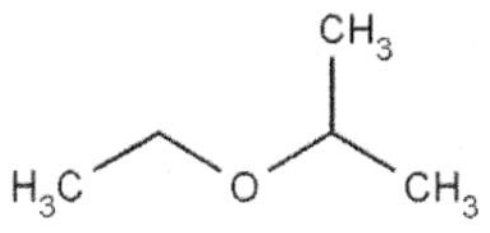

24. What compound is formed by the oxidation of 2-hexanol?

A. hexanal

B. hexanoic acid

C. 2-hexanone

D. 2-hexene

E. hexyne

25. Which of the following would have the highest boiling point?

A. 1-hexyne

B. 1-hexene

C. hexane

D. 1-hexanol

E. 1-pentanol

26. The functional group C=O is in all the species below, EXCEPT:

A. amides

B. ethers

C. aldehydes

D. ketones

E. esters

27. Which of the following is an allylic alcohol?

A. $CH_3CH=CHCH_2OH$

B. $HOCH=CHCH_2CH_3$

C. $CH_2=CHCH_2CH_3$

D. $CH_2=CHCH_2OCH_3$

E. $CH_2=CHCH_2CH_2OH$

28. Which of the following molecules has the most acidic proton?

A. 2-pentanol

B. 3-pentyne

C. 2-pentene

D. pentane

E. *tert*-butanol

29. What is the major product of this reaction?

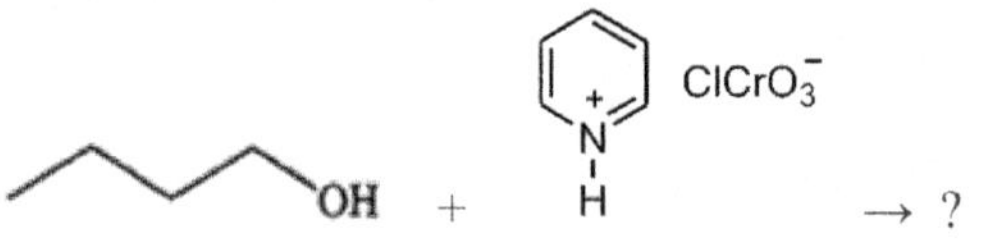

A.

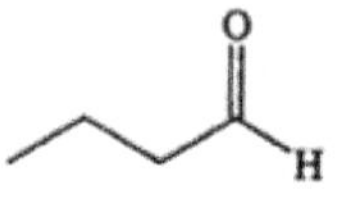

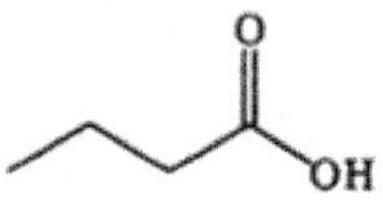

C.

B.

D.

E.

30. Which of the following alcohols dehydrates with the fastest rate?

A.

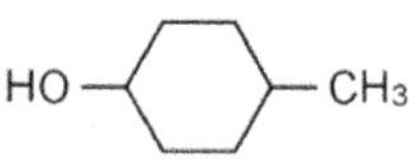

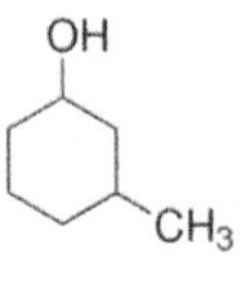

C.

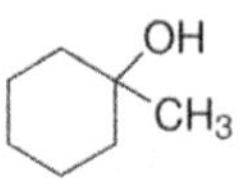

B.

D.

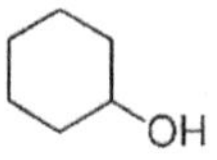

E.

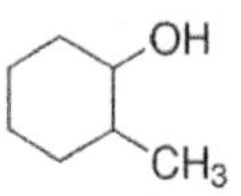

31. When (*R*)-2-heptanol is subjected to a two-step mechanism of tosyl chloride followed by Cl⁻, the product is:

A. (*R*)-2-chloroheptane

B. heptene

C. (*R/S*)-2-chloroheptane

D. (*S*)-2-chloroheptane

E. (*S*)-3-chloroheptane

32. Phenol exists predominantly:

A. in the keto form because its keto tautomer is antiaromatic

B. in the keto form because its keto tautomer is nonaromatic

C. in the enol form because its keto tautomer is antiaromatic

D. in the enol form because its keto tautomer is nonaromatic

E. in the keto form because its keto tautomer is aromatic

33. Treatment of salicylic acid with methanol and nonaqueous acid yields an:

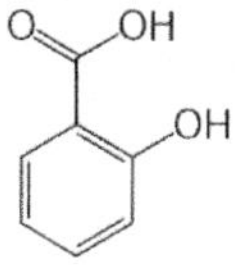

$+ CH_3OH + H_2SO_4 \rightarrow$?

Salicylic acid

A. acetal

B. ether

C. ester

D. hemiacetal

E. amide

34. When (*R*)-2-hexanol is subjected to PBr₃, the compound it produces is:

A. (*R*)-2-bromohexane

B. (*S*)-2-bromohexane

C. (*R/S*)-2-bromohexane

D. (*S*)-2-bromopentane

E. ketone

35. Which of the following reactions yields an ester?

A. $C_6H_5OH + CH_3CH_2Br$

B. $CH_3COOH + C_2H_5OH + H_2SO_4$

C. $CH_3COOH + SOCl_2$

D. $2CH_3OH + H_2SO_4$

E. $CH_3CH_2Br + CH_3CH_2O^-Na^+$

36. What is the major product of the reaction of 2,2-dimethylcyclohexanol with HBr?

A.

C.

B.

D.

E.

Notes for active learning

Notes for active learning

Answer Keys

and

Detailed Explanations

Answer Keys

Organic Chemistry Nomenclature

1: D	11: D	21: A	31: A	41: A
2: C	12: A	22: A	32: B	42: A
3: A	13: D	23: B	33: B	43: C
4: A	14: A	24: A	34: A	44: C
5: B	15: D	25: D	35: C	45: D
6: C	16: B	26: B	36: B	46: B
7: B	17: A	27: D	37: D	
8: D	18: E	28: B	38: A	
9: E	19: B	29: B	39: E	
10: B	20: B	30: C	40: C	

Covalent Bond

1: D	11: B	21: C	31: C	41: B
2: B	12: E	22: E	32: C	42: E
3: A	13: E	23: C	33: A	43: C
4: D	14: B	24: D	34: D	44: A
5: B	15: B	25: B	35: B	45: B
6: C	16: E	26: D	36: A	46: B
7: D	17: D	27: C	37: C	47: A
8: D	18: C	28: B	38: D	48: C
9: B	19: E	29: B	39: D	
10: B	20: E	30: E	40: B	

Stereochemistry

1: C	11: B	21: D	31: A	41: D
2: D	12: D	22: B	32: A	42: A
3: D	13: A	23: D	33: C	43: B
4: A	14: D	24: C	34: A	44: B
5: C	15: A	25: A	35: B	45: A
6: C	16: D	26: B	36: A	46: B
7: E	17: D	27: B	37: A	47: D
8: E	18: C	28: E	38: E	
9: B	19: A	29: D	39: C	
10: B	20: C	30: C	40: C	

Molecular Structure and Spectra

1: D	11: C	21: B	31: B
2: D	12: A	22: C	32: A
3: D	13: C	23: A	33: D
4: A	14: B	24: C	34: B
5: A	15: C	25: A	35: B
6: E	16: B	26: A	36: B
7: D	17: B	27: E	
8: E	18: C	28: A	
9: B	19: A	29: D	
10: C	20: A	30: E	

Alkanes and Alkyl Halides

1: C	11: D	21: C	31: D
2: D	12: D	22: D	32: B
3: B	13: D	23: B	33: A
4: D	14: C	24: C	34: B
5: E	15: B	25: C	35: D
6: A	16: D	26: A	36: E
7: B	17: D	27: D	
8: D	18: B	28: C	
9: C	19: B	29: A	
10: B	20: D	30: A	

Alkenes

1: C	11: A	21: E	31: B
2: B	12: C	22: A	32: A
3: D	13: A	23: C	33: A
4: D	14: A	24: C	34: A
5: D	15: C	25: A	35: C
6: A	16: D	26: A	36: A
7: A	17: A	27: E	
8: D	18: B	28: D	
9: A	19: D	29: A	
10: C	20: C	30: B	

Alkynes

1: E	11: C	21: B	31: D
2: C	12: D	22: C	32: A
3: C	13: B	23: D	33: C
4: A	14: A	24: C	34: C
5: A	15: C	25: D	35: C
6: D	16: B	26: B	36: B
7: B	17: D	27: D	
8: A	18: B	28: A	
9: C	19: C	29: C	
10: C	20: C	30: B	

Aromatic Compounds

1: C	11: C	21: B	31: A
2: B	12: A	22: D	32: A
3: E	13: D	23: C	33: B
4: D	14: C	24: D	34: C
5: A	15: D	25: C	35: A
6: D	16: E	26: C	36: D
7: C	17: A	27: A	
8: D	18: D	28: D	
9: A	19: C	29: D	
10: D	20: E	30: D	

Alcohols

1: B	11: B	21: D	31: D
2: E	12: C	22: D	32: D
3: C	13: C	23: D	33: C
4: E	14: B	24: C	34: B
5: A	15: A	25: D	35: B
6: C	16: B	26: B	36: B
7: B	17: E	27: A	
8: D	18: B	28: A	
9: B	19: D	29: A	
10: A	20: D	30: C	

Organic Chemistry Nomenclature – Detailed Explanations

1. D is correct.

The longest carbon chain is composed of seven carbon atoms.

There are chlorine, ethyl, and methyl substituents.

2. C is correct.

The longest carbon chain is composed of six carbon atoms and is the cyclohexene substructure.

The molecule contains a methyl group ($\sim CH_3$) in the fourth position.

3. A is correct.

One option is to draw the atoms to determine the atom count.

Alternatively, using a subscript of n for the number of carbons, the degrees of unsaturation can be determined from the following formulae:

> Alkane: C_nH_{2n+2} = 0 degrees of unsaturation
>
> Alkene: C_nH_{2n} = 1 degree of unsaturation
>
> Alkyne: C_nH_{2n-2} = 2 degrees of unsaturation
>
> Rings = 1 degree of unsaturation

The reference molecule has 2 rings and therefore 2 degrees of unsaturation:

> C_nH_{2n-2}
>
> $C_8H_{16-2} = C_8H_{14}$

4. A is correct.

The *para* notation means two substituents are on opposite sides of the aromatic rings in a C_1–C_4 relationship.

When the bromine atoms are adjacent (C_1–C_2), the isomer is *ortho*.

When the bromine atoms are in a C_1–C_3 relationship, the isomer is *meta*.

5. B is correct.

The longest carbon chain in the molecule has 4 carbon atoms, and therefore the root is *but–*.

An alkene is positioned at the second carbon with a suffix of *–ene*.

6. C is correct.

The longest carbon chain is composed of five carbon atoms.

The highest priority group is an aldehyde.

The substituent groups are the hydroxymethyl group, the ethyl group, the alkene, and the alkyne.

7. B is correct.

The cyclohexane is the longest carbon chain, and the alcohol is the highest priority group, making the root name *cyclohexanol*.

The chlorine and methyl groups are the substituents.

8. D is correct.

The alcohol of this aromatic compound has the highest priority, and the carbon count starts at this position. The root (and suffix) name of the compound is "phenol."

The ethyl group is numbered as three instead of four because the numbering favors the lower position values.

9. E is correct.

The longest carbon chain of the molecule is the 3-carbon propane.

There are three substituents in this molecule: two methyl groups are on the nitrogen atom, and one methyl group is at the second position.

10. B is correct.

The highest priority groups are *trans* to one another.

The longest carbon chain has seven carbon atoms, and the alkene is in the fourth position (fourth carbon from the alcohol, which is the highest priority group).

11. D is correct.

The longest carbon chain contains five carbons.

The highest priority group is the alcohol, so the name has –*ol* as the suffix and *pent*– as the root name.

The methyl substituent is in the second position.

12. A is correct.

Propyl substituents contain a three-carbon chain. If the point of attachment (indicated by the squiggle line) is at the second carbon, the group is an *iso*propyl group.

B: *tert-* butyl

C: *sec*-butyl

D: isobutyl

E: neopentyl

isopropyl   sec-butyl   isobutyl

tert-butyl   Isopentyl   neopentyl   tert-pentyl
               or isoamyl   or tert-amyl

Common names of alkyl substituents (recognized by IUPAC)

13. D is correct.

A: the molecule is *ortho*-fluorobenzoic acid.

B: the substituents should be given the lowest numbering and alphabetized to give 2-chloro-1,3-dinitrobenzene.

C: the substituents should be alphabetized to give 1-bromo-2-iodobenzene.

14. A is correct.

The longest chain is the cyclohexane; the chlorines are on the same side (*cis*) and are three carbons (1,3) apart.

15. D is correct.

The longest carbon chain has five carbon atoms.

The alcohol is attached to the carbon in the second position and the methyl to the carbon in the fourth position.

16. B is correct.

The longest carbon chain is a four-carbon cyclo derivative (i.e., cyclopentane).

There are four substituents located at the first and third positions in the molecule.

17. A is correct.

Draw the line formula of the carbon chain from the proper interpretation of the subscripts.

$$H-\overset{\overset{\displaystyle H}{|}}{\underset{\underset{\displaystyle H}{|}}{C}}-\overset{\overset{\displaystyle H}{|}}{\underset{\underset{\displaystyle H}{|}}{C}}-\overset{\overset{\displaystyle H}{|}}{\underset{\underset{\displaystyle H}{|}}{C}}-\overset{\overset{\displaystyle H}{|}}{\underset{\underset{\displaystyle H}{|}}{C}}-\overset{\overset{\displaystyle H}{|}}{\underset{\underset{\displaystyle H}{|}}{C}}-\overset{\overset{\displaystyle H}{|}}{\underset{\underset{\displaystyle H}{|}}{C}}-\overset{\overset{\displaystyle H}{|}}{\underset{\underset{\displaystyle H}{|}}{C}}-H$$

There are two methyl groups and five methylene ($\sim CH_2\sim$) in the molecule for seven carbons.

Use the following formula to calculate the degrees of unsaturation:

C_nH_{2n+2}: for an alkane (0 degrees of unsaturation)

18. E is correct.

The longest carbon chain is composed of five carbon atoms.

There are two alkenes, so the root name is "pentadiene."

There is a methyl group in the second position along the carbon chain.

19. B is correct.

Because the group has three carbon atoms, the group is a *propyl group*.

Propyl substituents exist as the *n*-propyl (i.e., *normal* or straight chain) or *isopropyl group*.

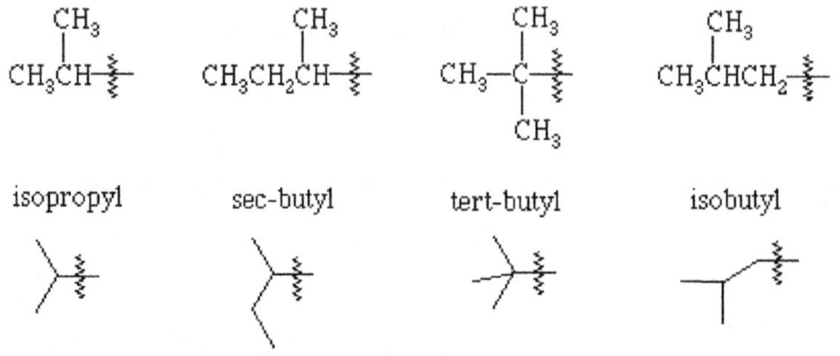

Sample common names for organic substituents used in the nomenclature

20. B is correct.

The longest carbon chain has six carbon atoms.

There are two methyl substituents in the molecule, and there is an isopropoxide substituent at the C4 position.

The stereochemistry of the alkene is *E*.

21. A is correct.

The molecule has four carbon atoms and two alkenes, hence the root name butadiene.

The double bonds of alkenes are in the first and third positions of the carbon chain.

22. A is correct.

The carboxylic acid (*–oic* acid) is considered the 1 position.

The hydroxyl group is in the *ortho* or the two positions.

23. B is correct.

The word *acetone* has two important components.

The *ace* is similar to *acetyl* and indicates that the structure includes a methyl group bonded to a carbonyl group.

The suffix *–one* indicates that the carbonyl group is a ketone.

24. A is correct.

The name above is the common name for the compound (i.e., toluene is the suffix for a benzene ring with a methyl substituent).

For IUPAC, the longest carbon chain in the compound is the six-membered benzene ring.

There are two substituent groups present in the molecule: the ethyl group and the methyl group.

The IUPAC name is 1-ethyl-3-methylbenzene

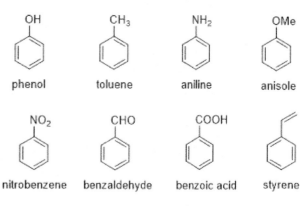

Common names for benzene derivatives

25. D is correct.

Cyclopropane is the only compound listed that contains three carbons.

All other answer choices have four carbons.

Cyclopropane with the stereochemistry of hydrogens indicated

26. B is correct.

The longest carbon chain in the molecule is six carbon atoms long.

The two methyl substituents are at the second and fourth positions in the chain.

27. D is correct.

The longest carbon chain that includes the double bond (i.e., alkene functional group) is a five-carbon molecule.

The chain is numbered with the alkene given the lowest number.

Ethyl (i.e., 2 carbon) substituent is at the second position in the carbon chain.

28. B is correct.

The longest carbon chain has 5 carbons and is cyclopentane – the root name of the molecule.

It possesses two substituent groups: the chloride and the methyl group.

Stereochemistry is indicated in the structure; the *cis-* notation is necessary for the compound's name.

29. B is correct.

Pentanal:

The longest carbon chain is five carbon atoms; the molecule contains an aldehyde, so the suffix is *–al*.

The suffix *–one* signifies a ketone, and *~oic acid* is for carboxylic acid.

30. C is correct.

The three substituent groups attached to the nitrogen atom include the two methyl and the *tert*-butyl group.

31. A is correct.

The longest carbon chain for this molecule is cyclohexene.

The highest priority group of the molecule is the carboxylic acid, and the carbon atom it is bonded to should be labeled as carbon one.

Therefore, the *oxo~* (i.e., prefix for the ketone) group is positioned at carbon two.

32. B is correct.

The longest carbon chain is composed of seven carbon atoms.

The remaining carbon groups are substituent methyl groups located at the second, fourth, and fifth positions along the carbon chain.

33. B is correct.

The longest chain of carbon atoms is the cyclohexane ring, hence the molecule's name.

There are two methyl substituents located at the first and second positions in the ring.

The groups are on the same side of the ring, so they have a *cis* orientation.

34. A is correct.

The longest carbon chain is 8 carbon atoms. The only substituent is the isopropyl group.

35. C is correct.

When numbering the longest carbon chain of a molecule, start on the end resulting in the lowest numbering for the substituent groups.

The correct molecule should have two methyl groups in the second position and one in the third position.

36. B is correct.

The longest carbon chain in the compound is composed of four carbon atoms.

The highest priority group in the molecule is the amine.

The amine is attached to carbon number 2 (i.e., *sec*-position).

The 5 common names recognized by IUPAC are isopropyl, isobutyl, *sec*-butyl, *tert*-butyl, and neopentyl.

2-butanamine is the IUPAC name for the molecule.

37. D is correct.

Draw the four-carbon chain with the double bond at the second position in the chain.

The second and third positions have a chlorine atom and are the highest priority substituents of the alkene.

They must be oriented on the same side of the double bond because the molecule is *cis*.

38. A is correct.

The longest continuous carbon chain is six atoms long, making it a substituted hexane chain.

The molecule contains a ketone carbonyl (designated by the suffix –*one*), with the carbon atoms numbered from the end of the chain closest to the carbonyl.

The ethyl substituent is located at carbon 3, while the carbonyl is at carbon 2.

Therefore, the IUPAC name for this molecule 3-ethylhexan-2-one.

39. E is correct.

The longest carbon chain is seven carbon atoms and includes an alkene.

The alkene is the highest priority functional group and is assigned the lowest number (i.e., 1 in this example).

Therefore, the molecule has a chlorine substituent in the fourth position.

40. C is correct.

The longest carbon chain is six carbon atoms.

The two substituents are the chlorine atom and the methyl group.

The highest priority group is chlorine and therefore assumes the lowest number.

41. A is correct.

The suffix ~*oate* signifies an ester functional group as the highest priority group in the molecule.

42. A is correct.

The longest carbon chain has seven carbon atoms; it has one chlorine and one methyl substituent.

IUPAC recognizes 5 common names in the nomenclature of organic molecules:

t-butyl   neopentyl   isopropyl

sec-butyl   isobutyl

43. C is correct. The longest carbon chain in the molecule is composed of seven carbon atoms.

The methyl substituent is at the fifth carbon of the chain.

The alkene *pi* bond is between carbon one and carbon two.

44. C is correct.

Neutral carbon atoms maintain bonds to four other atoms.

Therefore, an acyclic hydrocarbon cannot terminate with a methylene (~CH_2~) group.

Methyl groups are at the ends of alkanes and have a formula of ~CH_3.

Using a subscript of n for the number of carbons, the *degrees of unsaturation* can be determined from the following formulae:

　　　Alkane: C_nH_{2n+2} = 0 degrees of unsaturation

　　　Alkene: C_nH_{2n} = 1 degree of unsaturation

　　　Alkyne: C_nH_{2n-2} = 2 degrees of unsaturation

$CH_3CH_3CH_3$ has 3 carbons and, according to the formula C_nH_{2n+2}, should have 8 hydrogens.

This molecule has 9 hydrogens; it is impossible because it would require a carbon with 5 bonds.

A: $CH_3CHCH_3CH_2CH_3$ has 5 carbons and, according to the formula C_nH_{2n+2}, should have 12 hydrogens.

B: $CH_3CH_2CH_2CH_2CH_3$ has 5 carbons and, according to the formula C_nH_{2n+2}, should have 12 hydrogens.

D: $CH_3CH_2CH_2CH_3$ has 4 carbons and, according to the formula C_nH_{2n+2}, should have 10 hydrogens.

E: CH_3CH_3 has 2 carbons and, according to the formula C_nH_{2n+2}, should have 6 hydrogens.

45. D is correct.

Number this five-carbon chain from the highest-priority functional group – the alcohol (functional groups with higher oxidation states are higher priority). Thus, alcohol is attached to carbon 1.

The C=C double bond is between carbons 2 and 3, and the C≡C triple bond is between carbons 4 and 5.

The stereochemistry of the alkene is '*E*' (highest priority groups are on opposite sides of the alkene).

The priority groups are ranked according to the Cahn-Ingold-Prelog rules for prioritization based on the atomic number of atoms attached to the alkene.

Cis–trans relationship cannot be used to describe the molecule because the substituents across the double bond are different.

46. B is correct.

The longest carbon chain in the molecule contains six carbon atoms.

The highest (and only) functional group is the amide.

Notes for active learning

Notes for active learning

Notes for active learning

Covalent Bond – Detailed Explanations

1. D is correct.

The *benzylic* position is one carbon away from benzene or an aromatic ring. Without the aromatic ring, the cation is considered an *allylic* carbocation when one carbon from a double bond.

Vinyl means on the double bond.

2. B is correct.

The hydrogen atom bonds by overlapping its $1s$ orbital with the orbital of a bonding partner. The carbon atom is bonded to three atoms and is positively charged; indications that the carbon atom is sp^2 hybridized.

3. A is correct.

Using the formula for calculating the degrees of unsaturation reveals that 2 unsaturation elements (i.e., rings or *pi* bonds) exist.

Structures that contain atoms with satisfied octets are favored.

Molecules with charged carbon atoms tend to be less stable.

4. D is correct.

Wohler's experiment is significant because it demonstrated that organic compounds could be created from inorganic compounds. This result ran counter to the belief that the material that composed life was different from the matter of nonliving things, a theory called vitalism.

5. B is correct.

The *allylic cation* is a carbocation one *sigma* bond away from a double bond (i.e., alkene).

Resonance hybrids of an allylic carbocation

Methylene groups are points of saturation in the molecule that can prevent the conjugation of nearby alkenes.

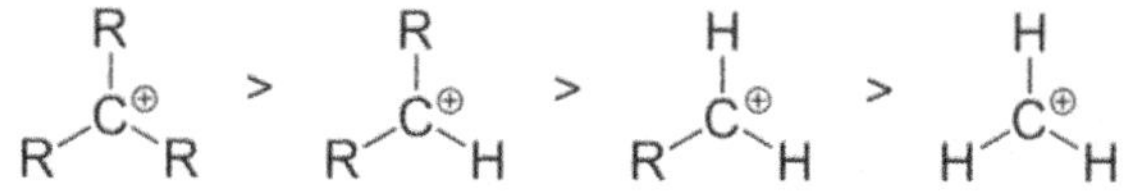

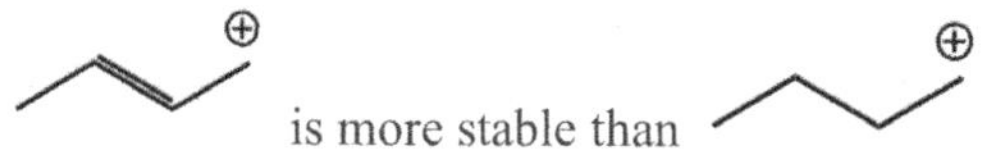

is more stable than

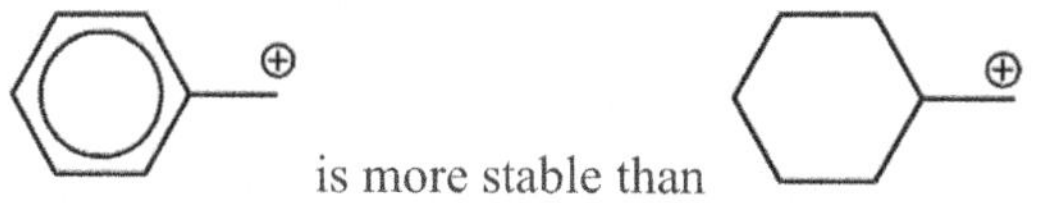

is more stable than

6. C is correct.

Propene is an example of an alkene, which have bonding angles of about 120 degrees.

This molecular geometry affords the substituent groups the greatest amount of spatial separation to minimize the intramolecular Van der Waals repulsions among them.

7. D is correct.

The electronegativity difference decides the distribution of electrons between bonded atoms.

This unequal distribution of electrons creates the polarity (∂^+ and ∂^-) of the bond.

8. D is correct.

The molecular formula given above is for an acyclic alkyne.

Acyclic alkynes have a linear geometry (i.e., 180 degrees), and the carbon atoms have a *sp* hybridization.

Cyclic alkynes have two fewer hydrogen atoms because those bonds are replaced with carbon-carbon bonds to form a ring.

9. B is correct.

Tertiary carbocations are more stable than *secondary* and *primary benzylic* carbocations, which are more stable than *primary* or *vinylic* carbocations.

Methyl cations are the least stable of the carbocations.

10. B is correct.

Nodes only form between the orbitals of atoms if the orbital phases have the opposite sign.

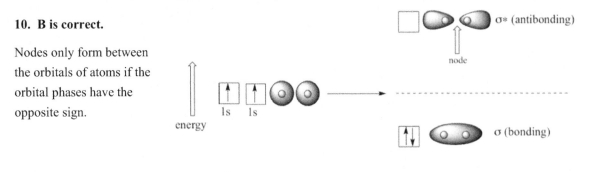

Atomic orbitals   *Molecular orbitals*

11. B is correct.

As the number of covalent bonds (i.e., triple > double > single) increases between carbon atoms, the bond order and strength increase.

Stronger bonds are shorter, so the two carbon atoms that make up the triple bond have the shortest bond.

12. E is correct.

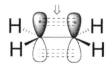

pi bond overlap between the unhybridized orbitals is indicated by the arrow

In organic molecules, the overlap of *pi* bonds is responsible for the formation of carbon-carbon *pi* bonds.

The orbitals of double and triple bonds (alkenes and alkynes, respectively) are unhybridized and are more reactive than the *sigma* bonds of single bonds.

Therefore, the reactions of alkenes typically involve breaking the alkene double bond.

13. E is correct.

Reasonable resonance forms do not allow nuclei to change positions and satisfy the octet rule.

Hydrogen can only have one bond, and carbon can only have four bonds based on the valence numbers.

Negative charges should be placed on more electronegative atoms.

14. B is correct.

The nitrogen atom does not contain a formal charge (the formal charge calculation for this atom is 0).

However, the charge is slightly negative because the nitrogen atom withdraws electron density from substituent groups *via* induction, and the lone pair represents a region of electron density.

15. B is correct.

Compounds that tend to be polar possess electronegative heteroatoms and more carbon-heteroatom bonds. If these groups can ionize to form charges, then they become even more polar.

16. E is correct.

For symmetric compounds like acetylene, no molecular dipole moment exists because the electron density is evenly distributed on either side of the triple bond.

Asymmetric molecules have molecular dipoles.

17. D is correct.

Except for structure D, the other structures are intermediates for electrophilic aromatic substitution.

These resonance intermediates typically have one cation and no negative charges in the ring.

continued…

Resonance hybrids of aniline during electrophilic aromatic substitution

18. C is correct.

The bonds between atoms (i.e., intramolecular) are stronger than bonds between molecules (i.e., intermolecular).

Examples of intermolecular bonds are hydrogen, dipole-dipole, dipole-induced dipole, and van der Waals.

Sigma bonds are single bonds and involve overlap along the internuclear axis between the atoms. S*igma* bonds are stronger than the *pi* bond of a double bond.

A: *hydrogen bonding* is a common intramolecular bond in which a *hydrogen* atom of one molecule is attracted to an electronegative atom (nitrogen, oxygen, or fluorine).

B: *dipole-dipole* bonds are attractive forces between the positive end of one polar molecule and the negative end of another polar molecule.

D: *ionic bonds* result from the complete transfer of valence electron(s) between atoms; it generates two oppositely charged ions. The metal loses electrons to become a positively charged cation, whereas the nonmetal accepts those electrons to become a negatively charged anion.

Ionic bonds can be disrupted in water and much weaker in aqueous solutions than in a dry environment.

19. E is correct.

The nitrogen lone pairs of amines (e.g., pyrrole) are sp^3 hybridized unless there is a *pi* bond between the nitrogen and carbon atom (e.g., pyridine).

Pyrrole has an sp^3 hybridized nitrogen (lone pair in the ring)

The nitrogen lone pair on pyridine is in an sp^2 hybridized orbital and is not a part of the aromatic system.

Pyridine has a sp^2 hybridized nitrogen (lone pair outside the ring)

20. E is correct.

Only the hydrogen atom can bond to other atoms with its unhybridized $1s$ orbital.

The *sigma* bonding is described by the hybridization of their atomic orbitals before bonding with other atoms.

Therefore, when a carbon atom forms a *sigma* bond, it does so by overlapping one of its hybridized orbitals.

However, *pi* bonding involves the indirect overlap of unhybridized p orbitals.

21. C is correct.

Multiple bonds and rings introduce degrees of unsaturation.

Using a subscript of n for the number of carbons, the *degrees of unsaturation* is determined by:

Alkane: C_nH_{2n+2} = 0 degrees of unsaturation

Alkene: C_nH_{2n} = 1 degree of unsaturation

Alkyne: C_nH_{2n-2} = 2 degrees of unsaturation

Rings = 1 degree of unsaturation

Double bonds = 1 degree of unsaturation

There is one degree of unsaturation for this compound (the ring).

With no other degrees of unsaturation present, there are no alkenes or double bonds present in the molecule.

22. E is correct.

Hydrogen atoms only bond with other atoms using their $1s$ orbital.

The nitrogen atoms hybridize their atomic orbitals to produce sp^3 orbital hybrids for bonding.

sp^3 orbitals are used because the nitrogen atom forms bonds of equal length with 4 other atoms.

23. C is correct.

The bond dipole in H–F is the largest because of the large difference in electronegativity between hydrogen and fluorine. The electrostatic attraction pulls the atoms closer, so the bond is the shortest and the strongest.

The bond dipole in H–I is the smallest because the electronegativity between the atoms is the lowest; therefore, H–I bond is the longest and weakest.

24. D is correct.

Tertiary carbocations are more stable than secondary carbocations, which are more stable than primary.

Carbocation stability: 3° > 2° > 1° > methyl

The more substituted the cation, the more it benefits from hyperconjugation stabilizing factors.

25. B is correct.

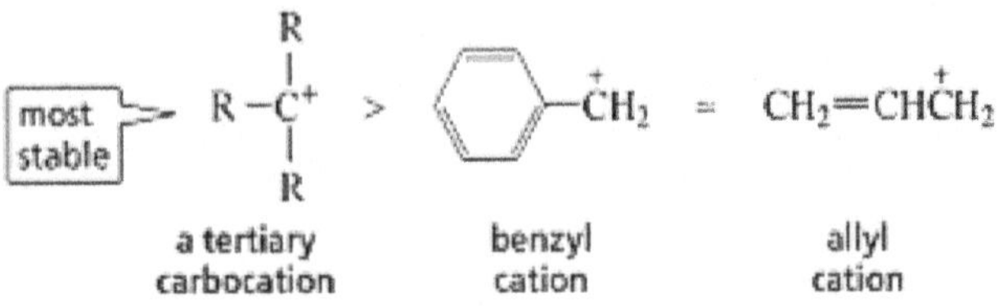

Carbocations are stabilized by resonance and by hyperconjugation.

The phenyl ring offers additional stability due to resonance structures with the delocalization of the pi electrons.

The primary non-conjugated carbocation (shown below) will be the least stable (except vinyl cation).

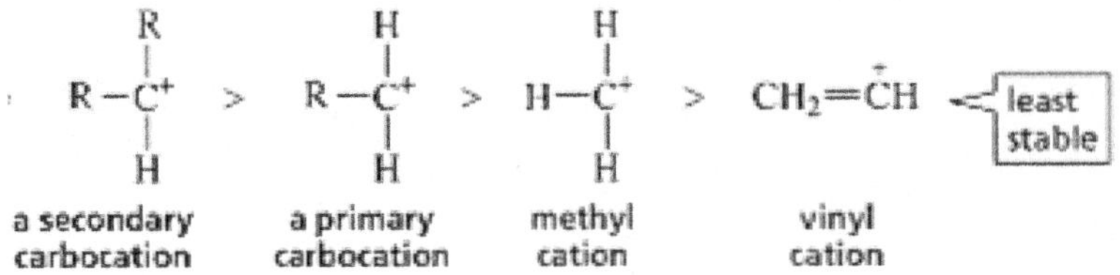

Relative stabilities of carbocations

26. D is correct.

The hybridized orbital is a combination of one *s* and three *p* orbitals.

Therefore, the energy of the hybridized orbital is between the energy of the combined orbitals.

The *s* orbital has lower energy than the *p* orbital.

27. C is correct.

The two allylic cations are resonance forms of each other.

Resonance involves the movement of conjugated *pi* systems, not of the atoms.

A and B are constitutional isomers (i.e., same molecular formula, but different connectivity).

28. B is correct.

$$H_3C - C(=O) - NH_2$$

acetamide

The conjugation observed (shown below) for carboxylic acids and their derivatives (i.e., acetamide) causes the carbonyl to adopt a bond length that is between a C–O single and C=O double bond.

Resonance structures of acetamide

The orbitals involved in resonance are the filled, donating *p* orbital of the nitrogen atom and the adjacent electron-accepting carbonyl *pi** orbital.

29. B is correct.

Acetylene is the common name for ethyne (C_2H_2). Alkynes are linear with a bond angle of 180°.

$$H-C\equiv C-H$$

Acetylene has a triple bond and therefore contains sp hybridized carbons.

A carbon of a triple bond is *sp* hybridized (i.e., *sp* + 2 unhybridized *p* orbitals).

Atoms in triple bonds use *sp* hybridized orbitals from the 2*s* orbital merging (i.e., hybridizing) with a 2*p* orbital.

A: 1,3,5–heptatriene contains sp^2 hybridized orbitals (i.e., double bonds) and sp^3 orbitals for single bonds. Bond angles of 120° are trigonal planar and originate from sp^2 orbitals. The molecule has single bonds, sp^3; a portion of the molecule is tetrahedral.

C: 2-butyne is an alkyne, but only two carbons are *sp* hybridized, while the remaining carbon is sp^3 hybridized, which results from the combination of the 2*s* and the 2*p* orbitals.

Four sp^3 carbons form and the bond angle is 109.5° with tetrahedral geometry.

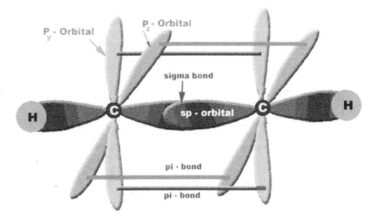

Molecular orbital structure for ethyne showing one sigma bond and two pi bonds.

D: dichloromethane has carbon sp^3 hybridized because it is attached to two hydrogens and two chlorine atoms.

The geometry is tetrahedral for the greatest separation between the substituents, and the bond angle is 109.5°.

continued…

E: 1,3-hexadiene contains sp^2 hybridized orbitals (i.e., double bonds) and sp^3 for single bonds. Bond angles of 120° are trigonal planar and originate from sp^2 orbitals.

The molecule contains single bonds, sp^3; therefore, a portion of the molecule is tetrahedral.

30. E is correct.

Six *sigma* bonds connect the carbon atoms in benzene.

Furthermore, the delocalized *pi* electron density in the ring; by three *pi* bonds in resonance.

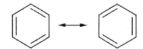

Two resonance Kekule structures of benzene

31. C is correct.

Draw each bond where the electrons are distributed to satisfy the octets of the carbon and heteroatoms:

$$CH_3C{\equiv}N$$

The nitrile has a triple bond composed of a *sigma* bond and two *pi* bonds.

32. C is correct.

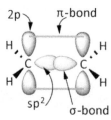

ethene

Hybridization and sigma and pi bonds indicated

Hybridization	Bond angle	Geometry
sp^3	109.5°	tetrahedral
$sp^2 + p$ (unhybridized)	120°	trigonal planar (flat)
$sp + p + p$ (two unhybridized)	180°	linear

33. A is correct.

In carbon–carbon double bonds, there is an overlap of sp^2 orbitals and a p orbital on the adjacent carbon atoms.

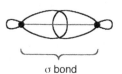

The sp^2 orbitals overlap head-to-head as a *sigma* (σ) bond, whereas the p orbitals overlap sideways as a *pi* (π) bond.

σ bond

Sigma bond formation showing electron density along the internuclear axis

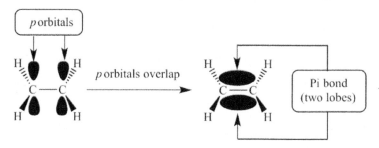

Two pi orbitals showing the pi bond formation during sideways overlap – note the absence of electron density (i.e., node) along the internuclear axis.

Bond lengths and strengths (σ or π) depend on the size and shape of the atomic orbitals and the density to overlap effectively.

The σ bonds are stronger than π bonds because head-to-head orbital overlap involves more shared electron density than sideways overlap.

The σ bonds formed from two $2s$ orbitals are shorter than those formed from two $2p$ or two $3s$ orbitals.

Carbon, oxygen, and nitrogen are in the second period ($n = 2$), while sulfur (S), phosphorus (P), and silicon (Si) are in the third period.

S, P, and Si use $3p$ orbitals to form π bonds, while C, N, and O use $2p$ orbitals.

The $3p$ orbitals are much larger than $2p$ orbitals, and a reduced probability for overlap of the $2p$ orbital of C and the $3p$ orbital of S, P, and Si.

B: S, P, and Si can hybridize, but these elements can combine s and p orbitals and (unlike C, O, and N) have d orbitals.

C: S, P and Si (ground-state electron configurations) have partially occupied p orbitals which form bonds.

D: carbon combines with elements below the second row of the periodic table.

For example, carbon commonly forms bonds with higher principal quantum number ($n > 2$) halogens (e.g., F, Cl, Br and I).

34. D is correct.

Draw the C–H bonds for this compound.

Each carbon atom of cyclohexane bonds to two hydrogen atoms with is one degree of unsaturation (the ring).

Six *sigma* bonds exist in the ring, so the number of σ bonds is 18.

35. B is correct.

There are four regions of electron density around the nitrogen atom (including the lone pair). Therefore, the nitrogen atom is *sp³* hybridized.

The bonding angles of molecules that possess nonbonding lone pairs of electrons are slightly smaller than what is predicted by the hybridization state. The nonbonding electrons exert a greater repulsive force than the bonding electrons between the central atom and the substituent groups.

However, bulky ethyl substituents increase the bond angle from approximately 107° to approximately 109.5°.

Ammonia has a bond angle of approximately 107° due to the electrostatic repulsion of the nitrogen's lone pair on the hydrogen atoms.

In amines, as substituents become larger (e.g., $(CH_3CH_2)_3N$), the bond angle between bulky groups increases, and the molecular shape approaches a tetrahedral with a bond angle of approximately 109.5°.

36. A is correct.

Three degenerate *p* orbitals exist for an atom with an electron configuration in the second (n = 2) shell or higher. The first (n = 1) shell only has an *s* orbital. The *d* orbitals become available from the third shell (n = 3).

37. C is correct.

The dipole moment is determined by the magnitudes of the individual bond dipoles and the spatial arrangement of the substituents on the molecule.

The dipole moment is greatest when there is a large difference in electronegativity of the bonded atoms. Therefore, a carbon–carbon bond (i.e., same electronegativity) has no dipole moment, while carbon–halogen bonds have moderately large dipole moments because of the electronegativity difference between carbon and halogen.

(1*R*,2*S*)-1,2-dichloro-1,2-diphenylethane is effectively *cis* due to restricted rotation.

continued…

(1*R*,2*S*)-1,2-dichloro-1,2-diphenylethane has two phenyl rings attached on one side and two chlorine groups attached on the other side.

The (*R/S*)–designation indicates that the two highest priority substituents (i.e., chlorine) are attached to the same side (priority according to molecular weight, so chlorine has higher priority). The highly electronegative chlorines pull electron density, creating a net dipole.

A: (1*S*,2*S*)-1,2-dichloro-1,2-diphenylethane contains only single bonds. The (*R/S*)–designation indicates that the two highest priority substituents (i.e., chlorine) are attached on opposite sides (with restricted rotation due to the size of the phenyl substitutes). The highly electronegative chlorines pull electron density in different spatial orientations, canceling a net dipole.

B: 1,2-dichlorobutane has carbon–chlorine highly polar bonds, but free rotation about the carbon–carbon single bond cancels any net dipole.

D: (*E*)-1,2-dichlorobutene differs from the *Z* configuration (or 1*R*,2*S* in the correct answer) because the two highest priority substituents are on opposite sides of the double bond. As the chlorine pulls electron density, dipoles cancel for a net dipole of zero.

E: (*Z*)-1,2-dibromobutene is the *Z* configuration (or 1*R*,2*S* in the correct answer) because the two highest priority substituents are on the same side of the double bond. However, bromine is less electronegative than chlorine and therefore has a smaller net dipole.

38. D is correct.

Benzene with sigma and pi bonds shown.

39. D is correct.

Formal charge = group # – nonbonding electrons – ½ bonding electrons

Nitrogen is in group V on the periodic table.

The ammonium cation has four bonds or eight bonding electrons.

The formal charge for the nitrogen atom is $5 - 0 - 8/2 = +1$.

40. B is correct.

Pyrrolidine is not an aromatic compound, so the lone pair of electrons on nitrogen is available for bonding (i.e., function as a base).

The molecule is a secondary alkyl amine, and the nitrogen atom has sp^3 hybridization.

41. B is correct.

The carbonyl carbon is trigonal planar because the double-bonded carbon is sp^2 hybridized.

I: each of the two methyl carbons is sp^3 hybridized and tetrahedral.

III: none of the carbons have an unshared pair of electrons (i.e., carbanions) because carbanions are highly reactive and observed in a limited number of examples (e.g., Grignard reagent, Gillman reagent, acetylide anion) and are not present in stable molecules.

42. E is correct.

The allylic cation can delocalize the cation at the most substituted position is the most stable molecule.

The other allylic cations are not as stable because the cation is less substituted in the other resonance forms.

43. C is correct.

Resonance structures are derived from the movement of lone pairs and *pi* electrons.

Generated negative charges are placed on the more electronegative atoms and the positive charges on the less electronegative atoms.

44. A is correct.

The oxygen atom contains four regions of electron density (i.e., two lone pairs and two methyl substituents) and adopts a tetrahedral configuration.

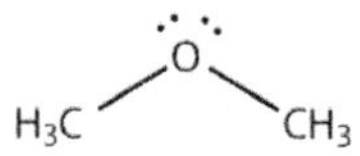

Dimethyl ether has an angle between substituent (i.e., methyl) groups of approximately 109.5 degrees.

45. B is correct.

There are four bonding patterns of carbon described by the three hybridization bonding models.

When carbon forms four single (σ) bonds, it is sp^3 hybridized.

When carbon forms one double (π) bond and two single (σ) bonds, it is sp^2 hybridized.

Carbon is sp hybridized when it forms one triple ($2-\pi$) bond and one single (σ) bond, or it forms two double (π) bonds.

O=CH–CH$_2$–CH=C=C=CH$_2$

  sp^2 sp^3 sp^2 sp sp sp^2

46. B is correct.

Full arrowheads show the movement of a pair of electrons (compared to single-headed – or *fishhook* – arrows for radical reactions).

The only movement of the *pi* (π) electrons is responsible for the stable diene structures to the right. The *pi* electrons must be in conjugation.

47. A is correct.

There are four regions of electron density around the nitrogen atom (including the lone pair). Therefore, the nitrogen atom is *sp³* hybridized.

Electron geometry describes the geometry of the electron pairs, groups, and domains on the central atom, whether they are bonding or non-bonding. Molecular geometry is the name of the shape used to describe the molecule.

When atoms bond to a central atom, they do it in a way that maximizes the distance between bonding electrons. This gives the molecule its overall shape. If no lone pairs of electrons are present, the electronic geometry is the same as the molecular shape.

A lone pair occupies more space than bonding electrons, so the net effect is to bend the shape of the molecule (electron geometry conforms to predicted shape).

The shape of this molecule is trigonal pyramidal with bonds of approximately 109.5 degrees due to the bulky ethyl substituents.

The three substituents (i.e., ethyl) and the lone pair on the nitrogen result in the pyramidal shape consistent with VESPER theory.

48. C is correct.

Tertiary carbocations are more stable than secondary or primary carbocation because they experience more hyperconjugation effects from neighboring C–H bonds.

Resonance stabilization lowers the energy of the cation.

Notes for active learning

Notes for active learning

Notes for active learning

Stereochemistry – Detailed Explanations

1. C is correct.

Draw the different isomers of butene.

This compound can be drawn with the double bond terminal (the carbons are numbered according to IUPAC).

The terminal carbon in the double bond is numbered 1.

There are two geometric isomers of butene (i.e., *cis*-butene and *trans*-butene).

cis-2-butene   *trans*-2-butene

Geometric isomers are a subset of structural isomers. Geometric requires that the substituents from the double bond can be the same (i.e., *cis* and *trans*) or different (i.e., *E* and *Z*).

1-butene or butene (the position 1 is implied by IUPAC)

Isobutylene (not 2-methyl propene) according to IUPAC

Therefore, there are four structural isomers of butene.

2. D is correct.

An *asymmetric carbon* refers to a chiral carbon: carbon bonded to four different substituents. The other compounds do not contain asymmetric carbons because at least two of the three atoms or groups bonded to each carbon atom are the same.

3. D is correct.

The number of stereoisomers for a given molecule depends on the number of asymmetric carbon atoms (or chiral centers) present.

There is a 2^N number of possibilities, where N is the number of chiral centers present.

The molecule has 4 chiral centers: $2^4 = (2 \times 2 \times 2 \times 2) = 16$ stereoisomers.

For some molecules, symmetry elements may be redundant structures, so the 2^N calculation gives the maximum number of stereoisomers and not necessarily the actual number that exists.

4. A is correct.

Remember: if an alkene has geminal disubstitution (i.e., two identical moieties bonded to the same alkene carbon), then *cis* and *trans* isomerism is not possible.

5. C is correct.

The naming reveals that the compounds are the same: 7-ethyl-4-isopropyl-3,6-dimethyldecane

6. C is correct.

The bromine substitution changes from vicinal (on adjacent carbons) to geminal (on the same carbon). Because the connectivity changes, the structures are constitutional isomers.

The first molecules cannot be chiral because it has a mirror plane of symmetry.

7. E is correct.

The molecules shown above are mirror images of each other.

Assign *R* and *S* at each chiral center to evaluate the relationship between the two chiral molecules.

8. E is correct.

In *polarimeters* (i.e., plane-polarized light), enantiomers have the same magnitude of specific rotation but opposite sign.

9. B is correct.

Isomers are compounds with the same molecular formula but a different structure.

A: *hydrocarbons* are organic molecules containing only carbon and hydrogen (i.e., no heteroatoms such as oxygen or nitrogen).

C: *homologs* are a series of compounds with the same general formula, usually varying by a single parameter (e.g., length of the carbon chain).

D: *isotopes* have different mass numbers due to differences in the number of neutrons. The number of protons determines the identity of the element.

E: *allotropes* are each of two or more different physical forms in which an element can exist (e.g., carbon exists as graphite, charcoal, and diamond).

10. B is correct.

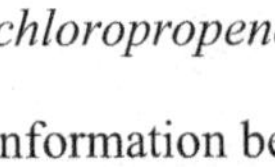

(Z)-1-bromo-1-chloropropene 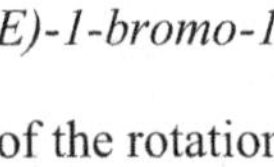   *(E)-1-bromo-1-chloropropene*

These molecules can only adopt one conformation because of the rotational barrier of the alkene.

continued…

Configurational isomers involve a double bond. If the molecules have optical activity, they may be enantiomers (non-superimposable mirror images) or diastereomers. If they lack optical activity, they are *geometric isomers.*

A: *constitutional isomers* have the same molecular formula but different connectivity. The molecules are not the same, but the connectivity is the same, so they are not constitutional isomers.

C: *identical molecules* may be drawn with different orientations on the paper but are the same.

D: *conformational isomers* refer to different molecules due to free rotation around single bonds (e.g., Newman projections, chair flips for cyclohexane).

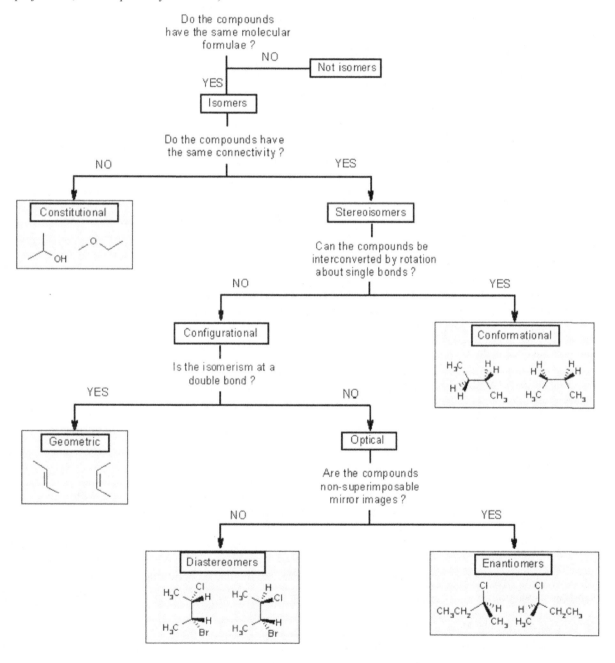

11. B is correct.

Chiral carbons refer to asymmetric carbons typically bonded to three other atoms.

Carbon 2 cannot be an asymmetric carbon (or chiral carbon) because carbon atoms with trigonal planar configuration possess a plane of symmetry and are achiral.

12. D is correct.

The number of stereoisomers depends on chiral centers, defined as a carbon bonded to 4 different substituents.

The number of possible stereoisomers is 2^n, where n is the number of chiral centers.

Number the carbons with the carbonyl carbon as #1.

Carbons 1 and 6 are not chiral centers because carbon 1 is attached to only three substituents, while carbon 5 has two identical hydrogen substituents.

Carbons 2, 3, 4, and 5 are chiral centers since each is bonded to 4 different groups.

Therefore, the molecule has 4 chiral centers, and the number of stereoisomers is $2^4 = 2 \times 2 \times 2 \times 2 = 16$.

13. A is correct.

These molecules are isomers because they have the same number and atoms, but the bonding is different.

B: *epimers* are two isomers that differ in configuration at only one stereogenic center. Stereocenters in epimer molecules, if any, are the same.

C: *anomers* are diastereoisomers for cyclic sugars differing in the anomeric carbon configuration (C–1 atom of an aldose or the C–2 atom of a 2-ketose). The cyclic forms of carbohydrates can exist in α– or β–, based on the position of the substituent at the anomeric center. α–anomers have the hydroxyl pointing down, while β–anomers have the hydroxyl pointing up.

D: *allotropes* are two or more different physical forms in which an element can exist. Graphite, charcoal, and diamond are allotropes of carbon.

E: *geometric isomers* differ in the arrangement of groups about a double bond, ring, or other rigid structure.

14. D is correct.

The bromine and hydrogen atoms alternate the carbon atoms they are bonded to, so they are constitutional isomers. These molecules cannot be chiral because they have a mirror plane of symmetry.

15. A is correct.

The *anti*-conformer (180° offset) has the lowest energy because it minimizes steric strain (i.e., bulky substituents within van der Waals radii) and torsional strain (i.e., repulsion of bonding electrons when eclipsed).

Gauche refers to a dihedral angle of 60°.

diagrams below…

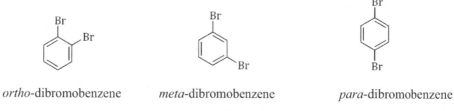

16. D is correct.

Draw each isomer and be cognizant of equivalent structures.

ortho-dibromobenzene   *meta*-dibromobenzene   *para*-dibromobenzene

There are only three isomers for the given molecular formula.

17. D is correct.

There are two ways to draw butane; the straight-chain or the tertiary alkyl constitutional isomer. Note that the term "constitutional isomers" is recognized by IUPAC, while "structural isomers" was common historically.

Two constitutional isomers of n-butane (left) and isobutene (right)

18. C is correct.

Geometric (configurational) isomers have the same molecular formula but different connectivity of atoms due to the orientation of substituents around a carbon-carbon double bond (or ring). In *Z* (*cis* when substituents are the same) isomers, identical substituents are on one side of the double bond or ring. In *E* (*trans* when substituents are the same) isomers, identical substituents are on opposite sides of the double bond or ring.

19. A is correct.

Isomers are molecules with the same molecular formula but different connections (e.g., functional groups) between the atoms. Therefore, the number of carbons, hydrogen and heteroatoms must be the same.

20. C is correct.

Cis means that the groups are on the same side of the alkene (or face of a cyclic structure).

Trans means that the groups are on opposite sides.

Cis and *trans* isomerism can occur with disubstituted cycloalkanes.

cis-2-butene   trans-2-butene

Cis and *trans* isomerism can occur with alkenes (or for a ring).

21. D is correct.

The number of each atom must be consistent among a pair or group of isomers, meaning that the oxidation state of the carbon atoms of the compound is consistent.

A change in the oxidation state of the compound suggests that the hydrogen count is different.

For instance, the isomer of the given alcohol is another alcohol and not an aldehyde or a ketone.

22. B is correct.

There are two stereoisomers for the vicinal disubstituted alkene (1,1-chlorofluoroethene), and there is only one isomer of the 1,2 disubstituted alkene (*cis* and *trans*).

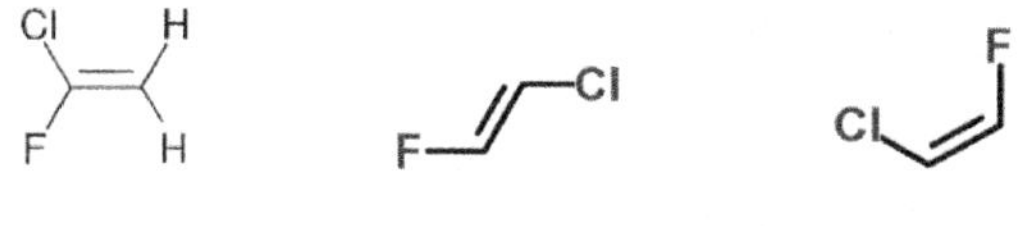

23. D is correct.

Use the rotation rule (clockwise = *R*, counterclockwise = *S*) to determine the configuration after assigning priorities. When the lowest priority group is on the horizontal bond, the assigned configuration is reversed.

24. C is correct.

Enantiomers are chiral molecules (i.e., attached to four different groups) and non-superimposable mirror images (i.e., *R* and *S*).

The two molecules are mirror images of each other, so they are enantiomers.

25. A is correct.

There are two stereoisomers for the vicinal disubstituted alkene (i.e., *cis* and *trans*).

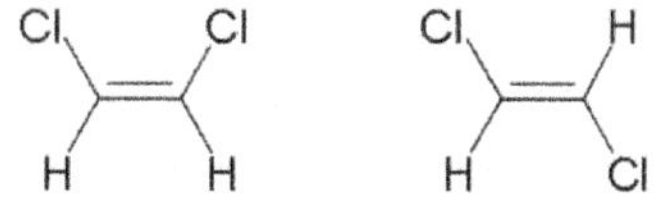

cis- and *trans*-dichloroethylene

There is only one isomer of the geminal (i.e., on the same atom) disubstituted alkene.

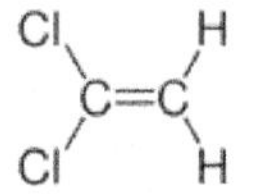

1,1-dichloroethene

26. B is correct.

To determine the enantiomer of the compound, draw the mirror image of the compound.

This requires inverting the two stereocenters, as inverting only one results in a diastereomer.

27. B is correct.

Meso compounds are molecules with chiral centers and require an inversion center or a plane of symmetry. These elements of symmetry make molecules with asymmetric carbon atoms achiral overall.

28. E is correct.

Any molecule that has a non-identical mirror image is chiral and has an enantiomer.

Draw the structure of the cyclic compound:

cis-1,2-dimethylcyclopentane

Comparison of the molecule reveals an internal plane of symmetry.

A *meso* compound and its enantiomer (i.e., a non-superimposable mirror image of a chiral molecule) are the same. Therefore, a *meso* compound does not have an enantiomer.

29. D is correct.

Structural isomers have the same molecular formula but a different connection to the atoms. With molecular formula $C_4H_8Cl_2$, the carbon skeleton is butane.

Eight structural isomers exist: three isomers have chiral carbons.

From top left and moving to the right: molecules 2, 3 and 6 are chiral (i.e., a carbon attached to four different substituents). Molecule 2 has one chiral carbon; molecule 3 has one chiral carbon. Structural isomer 6 contains two chiral carbons. One of the stereoisomers of 2,3-dichlorobutane has an internal plane of symmetry, making it the *meso* compound of R/S (or S/R, which is the same molecule) and therefore is achiral and optically inactive.

The other stereoisomer is R/R (or S/S, which is the same molecule) and therefore is chiral and exhibits optical activity.

Therefore, there are three optically active isomers of $C_4H_8Cl_2$.

30. C is correct.

Chiral carbon atoms have four different groups bonded to a carbon atom.

The molecule is named with the alcohol as the highest priority group and designated carbon 1.

The carbon atoms with two or more hydrogen atoms (i.e., carbons 1 and 5) are achiral because at least two groups are the same.

31. A is correct.

Achiral compounds cannot rotate the plane of polarized light.

The solutions of achiral compounds are optically inactive.

B: no relationship between absolute configuration (*R/S*) and specific rotation (+/−) of light in the polarimeter.

C: *meso* compounds are achiral, but not all achiral molecules are *meso*.

D and E: *meso* compounds are achiral, contain two or more chiral centers, and an internal plane of symmetry.

32. A is correct.

The stereochemistry of the alkene is '*E*' (highest priority groups are on opposite sides of the alkene).

The priority groups are ranked according to the Cahn-Ingold-Prelog rules for prioritization based on the atomic number of atoms attached to the alkene.

The chain possessing the heaviest atoms proximal to the alkene generally has higher priority. In this example, the bromomethyl group has a higher priority.

The alcohol and methoxy groups contain oxygen atoms, but the methoxy oxygen is closer to the double bond.

33. C is correct.

For Fischer projections, horizontal lines represent bonds projecting outward (i.e., wedges), whereas vertical lines represent bonds going back (i.e., dashed lines). A Fischer projection does not include a carbon specified at the cross of the vertical and horizontal lines (i.e., a C is implied, but no C is written on the structure).

For assigning *R/S* in Fischer projections, read the ranked (1 → 3) priorities as clockwise (*R*) or counterclockwise (*S*). If the lowest priority is vertical (i.e., points into the page), then assign *R/S*. If the lowest priority is horizontal (i.e., points out of the page), reverse (*R* → *S*, *S* → *R*).

Compound I: the order of priority is hydroxyl, carboxyl, methyl, and hydrogen. The order of increasing priority is counterclockwise, and the configuration appears S. However, the lowest priority (group 4 is H) is horizontal (pointing outward), so the absolute configuration is *R*.

Compound II: the order of priority is nitrogen, carboxyl, methyl, and hydrogen. The order of increasing priority is counterclockwise. The lowest priority (group 4 is H) is vertical and therefore points away. The absolute configuration is *S*.

continued…

Compound III is achiral because the carbon is not attached to four different groups, and therefore the molecule is neither *R* nor *S*.

Compound IV: the order of priority is hydroxyl, carbonyl (aldehyde), methyl (methanol), and hydrogen. The order of increasing priority is counterclockwise. The lowest priority (group 4 is H) is horizontal and therefore points towards the viewer. The absolute configuration is *R*.

Compounds I and IV have the same absolute configuration.

34. A is correct.

The root name of the compound is cyclopentane because the ring possesses 5 carbons.

The Cl substituents are adjacent (i.e., position 1,2) on the ring and must be oriented on opposite sides.

35. B is correct.

Chiral molecules include carbons bonded to four different substituents. This molecule contains no stereogenic centers (i.e., chiral centers), and therefore the molecule cannot be chiral.

36. A is correct. The observed rotation is half the value of the specific rotation for the pure enantiomeric substance. While the effect of the combined opposite enantiomers is canceled, the mixture should have a 50% excess of the pure substance.

The mixture must have 75% of the pure enantiomeric substance, where 25% of the rotation cancels the effect of the 25% opposite rotation of its enantiomer.

37. A is correct.

The carbon attached to the leaving group is tertiary (bonded to 3 carbons) and chiral because it is bonded to 4 different substituents, and the molecule is optically active. Tertiary alkyl halides undergo S_N1 reactions (forming a trigonal planar carbocation) but do not undergo S_N2 reactions because of steric hindrance.

In the first step of the S_N1 reaction, the bromine dissociates to form a stable tertiary carbocation, which results in the loss of optical activity. A positively charged carbon is sp^2 hybridized (trigonal planar) and achiral because it has only three substituents.

In the second step, the HCN nucleophile attacks the trigonal planar (flat) carbocation from either side of the plane (i.e., top or bottom) with approximately equal probability. As a result, the reaction yields approximately equal amounts of two chiral products.

The products are enantiomers (i.e., chiral molecules are non-superimposable mirror images), and each enantiomer rotates the plane of polarized light to the same extent but in opposite directions.

Therefore, the product is an optically inactive racemic mixture (i.e., both enantiomers in the solution), and there is a loss of optical activity in the solution.

Racemization means loss of optical activity and often involves a carbocation intermediate (S_N1 reaction), whereby the incoming nucleophile attacks from either side of the trigonal planar carbocation.

continued…

B: *mutarotation* occurs in monosaccharides (i.e., sugars) and involves the equilibrium between open-chain forms and cyclic hemiacetal forms (e.g., Haworth projections) in aqueous solutions.

D: *inversion* of absolute configuration only occurs in S_N2 reactions, whereby a nucleophile attacks the substrate from the side opposite the leaving group (backside) in a one-step reaction.

From the concerted S_N2 reaction, the products have the same absolute configuration (often inverted from the backside attack), and the product is considered chiral.

38. E is correct.

Draw the structure of each of the possibilities and count the number of isomers.

Two isomers can be formed from the geminal substitution of the chlorine atoms; three isomers result from the (1,2), (1,3), and (1,4) disubstitution.

The last isomer involves a (2,3) dichloro substitution.

The (2,3) disubstitution can exist as a pair of diastereomers.

39. C is correct.

An asymmetric (i.e., chiral) carbon is bonded to four different substituents.

There are three asymmetric carbons in this molecule.

The methylene is symmetrical; the isopropyl and the geminal dimethyl groups have symmetrical carbons.

40. C is correct.

Because one of the stereocenters has a different *R/S* configuration, the molecules are diastereomers.

41. D is correct.

A *meso* compound has chiral centers but is not chiral because it has an internal plane of symmetry.

Tartaric acid is a four-carbon polyol with two carboxylic acids and two chiral centers.

There are three stereoisomers: the (+) form, the (−) form, and the *meso* form.

Meso compounds are identical to their mirror images.

Each of the two stereoisomers rotates plane-polarized light as indicated by the notation of (+) or (−), but *meso*-tartaric acid is achiral (i.e., no net rotation of plane-polarized light).

III: *racemic mixtures* are solutions with enantiomers (i.e., chiral molecules that are mirror images).

A *meso* compound is a single molecule that contains two enantiomers joined.

42. A is correct.

A racemic mixture contains equal quantities of two enantiomers (i.e., isomers that are non-superimposable mirror images).

Compound I is D-fructose in a Fischer projection.

Compound II is D-fructose in a straight chain.

Compound III is D-glucose in a straight chain.

43. B is correct.

The molecule that contains the chiral carbon is the one that has a central carbon with four different groups as substituents. These carbons are described as asymmetric (i.e., stereogenic center or chiral carbons).

44. B is correct.

The chlorine atom occupies the internal (i.e., 2nd) carbon on the first molecule, and the chlorine atom is bonded to a terminal (i.e., 1st) carbon on the second molecule.

Constitutional (i.e., structural or configurational) isomers have the same molecular formula but different connectivity of the atoms.

A: *conformational* isomers involve free rotation around a single bond (e.g., Newman projections).

C: *diastereomers* are chiral molecules (i.e., attached to four different groups) with two or more chiral centers and are non-superimposable non-mirror images (i.e., *R,R* and *S,R*).

D: *enantiomers* are chiral molecules (i.e., attached to four different groups) and are non-superimposable mirror images (i.e., *R* and *S*).

The exception of the two or more chiral center requirements for diastereomers is geometric isomers that contain double bonds (i.e., *cis* and *trans*).

45. A is correct.

For an alkene to experience *cis-trans* isomerization, the *pi* bond of the double bond is broken.

The *pi* bond of the alkene makes the double bond rigid. Heating the alkene at high temperatures or exposure to electromagnetic radiation (e.g., UV radiation) may cause the *pi* bond to homolytically cleave to 1,2-diradical and rotate about the *sigma* bond to form the diastereomers.

E / *Z* and *cis* / *trans* isomers are geometric isomers and classified as diastereomers.

46. B is correct.

When determining whether an alkene is the *Z / E* (or *cis / trans*) stereoisomer, it is important to identify the higher priority substituent group at each of the two carbon atoms of the alkene.

The priority groups are ranked by the Cahn-Ingold-Prelog rules for prioritization based on the atomic number of atoms attached to the alkene.

If the higher priority groups are positioned on the same side of the double bond, the molecule is *Z* (*cis* notation can be used if the substituents are the same).

If the higher priority groups are positioned on the opposite sides of the double bond, the molecule is *E* (*trans* notation can be used if the substituents are the same).

The stereochemistry about the alkene is '*Z*.' The highest priority groups – Br and Cl across the double bond – are on the same side of the alkene.

Cis–trans relationship cannot be used to describe the molecule because the substituents across the double bond are different.

47. D is correct.

Determine the molecular formula of the given molecule. 2-methylbutane has 5 carbon atoms and 12 hydrogen atoms.

Only *n*-pentane has the same molecular formula.

The notation *n*– represents normal (or straight chain).

Notes for active learning

Notes for active learning

Notes for active learning

Molecular Structure and Spectra – Detailed Explanations

1. D is correct.

The local magnetic field generated by the circulating current of the benzene ring causes the protons attached to the ring to be further deshielded.

Electron-donating and withdrawing groups attached to the ring shift the resonances of protons up or downfield.

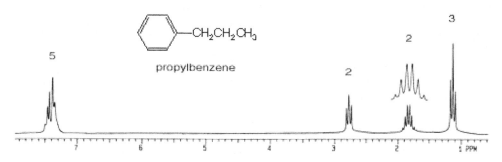

^{1}H NMR spectra with characteristic absorption for the phenyl ring between 6.0-8.0 ppm

2. D is correct.

The shielding effect arises from the electron density associated with the nuclei.

Hydrogen nuclei with more electron density are shielded, and their chemical shifts appear more upfield in the spectrum.

3. D is correct.

2-methylpropanoic acid

Carbonyl carbons show an IR absorption between approximately 1630 and 1780 cm^{-1}. The carbonyl of a carboxylic acid is reported to be between 1710 and 1780 cm^{-1}.

Because carboxylic acids contain a hydroxyl (~OH) group, another signal around 3300 to 3400 cm^{-1} should be expected in the spectrum for this compound.

4. A is correct.

5. A is correct.

The n to *pi** transition for ketones is the electron transition requiring the least energy.

Antibonding orbitals are vacant and serve as the acceptor orbitals for the electron excitation. The orbitals of nonbonding electrons have more energy than the orbitals for *pi* bonds.

Electron transitions from *sigma* bonds are difficult because electron energy is low and requires high energy to be promoted.

6. E is correct.

The peak area ratios of the spin states correspond to the values derived from Pascal's triangle.

The heights of the peaks may not correspond to the same ratio, but the area does.

n	2^n	multiplet intensities	
0	1	1	Singlet (s)
1	2	1 1	Doublet (d)
2	4	1 2 1	Triplet (t)
3	8	1 3 3 1	Quartet (q)
4	16	1 4 6 4 1	Pentet
5	32	1 5 10 10 5 1	Sextet
6	64	1 6 15 20 15 6 1	Septet
7	128	1 7 21 35 35 21 7 1	Octet
8	256	1 8 28 56 70 56 28 8 1	Nonet

Pascal's triangle

7. D is correct.

The most deshielded protons in the NMR spectrum have the largest δ shift (i.e., downfield).

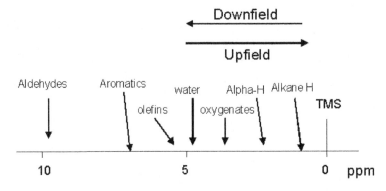

NMR with an approximate δ shift of some functional groups

8. E is correct.

The M–18 peak corresponds to the loss of water. The loss of water in a substrate containing alcohol may suggest that an alkene intermediate is generated during the ionization process.

9. B is correct.

The *alpha nitrogen* atom makes the neighboring C–H bonds less shielded because the nitrogen atom is electronegative and withdraws electron density through an inductive effect.

Terminal or substituted alkyl C–H bonds (away from electronegative atoms) resonate between 1 and 2 ppm.

10. C is correct.

3,3-dibromoheptane (below) produces 6 NMR signals.

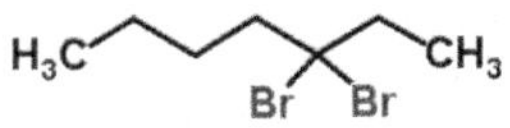

A: 1,1,2-tribromobutane (below) produces 4 NMR signals.

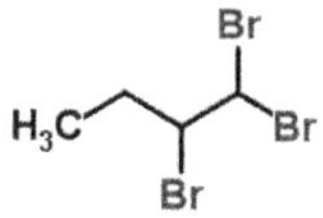

B: bromobutane (below) produces 4 NMR signals.

D: dibutyl ether (below) produces 4 NMR signals.

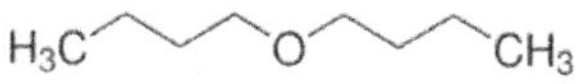

11. C is correct.

Molecules containing the carbonyl functional groups, such as ketones, typically have C=O resonance frequencies at 1710 cm^{-1}.

However, the stretching frequency is lower if the carbonyl group is in conjugation with another group (in this case, the alkene).

Resonance contributes to the carbon-oxygen single bond character of the carbonyl, and single bonds are weaker than double bonds.

12. A is correct.

The *topicity* of the protons can be determined by labeling them as H$_a$ and H$_b$ to produce a "chiral center." If this causes the molecule to have two or more chiral centers, then the protons are *diastereotopic*.

If the labeling causes the molecule to have only one stereocenter, the labeled protons are *enantiotopic*.

If labeling the protons as H$_a$ and H$_b$ does not lead to the formation of a chiral center (as in methane), then the protons are *homotopic*.

13. C is correct.

1-chlorobutane (below) has a chiral center and produces 4 NMR peaks.

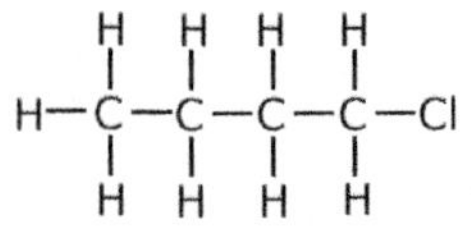

A: 3,3-dichloropentane (below) is a symmetrical molecule that produces 2 NMR proton peaks.

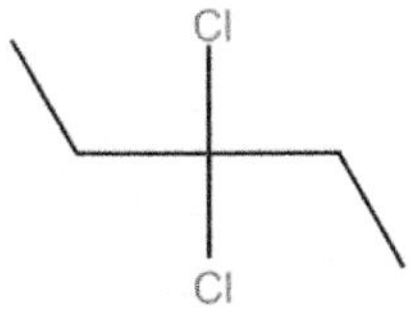

B: 4,4-dichloroheptane (below) is a symmetrical molecule that produces 3 NMR proton peaks.

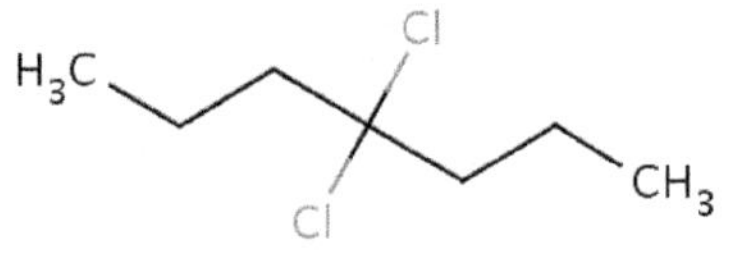

D: 1,4-dichlorobutane (below) produces 2 NMR proton peaks.

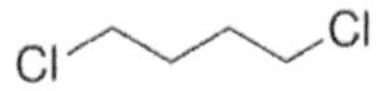

E: dichloromethane (below) produces 1 NMR proton peak.

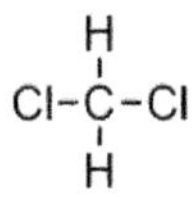

14. B is correct.

Carboxylic acid protons are some of the most deshielded protons.

These functional groups can partially ionize, causing the hydrogen to develop a high degree of positive (cationic) character.

15. C is correct.

The stretching frequency is much higher than a typical carbonyl group.

The chlorine atom is a poor electron donor to the carbonyl through lone pair conjugation, and it tends to withdraw more electron density through induction.

The lone pair of electrons on the oxygen atom can donate to carbon-chlorine *sigma* orbital, shortening the bond.

The shorter (or stronger) a bond, the higher is its stretching frequency in the IR spectrum.

If the lone pair conjugation with the carbonyl is the more dominant effect (e.g., amides), the carbonyl stretching frequency is lower than 1710 cm^{-1}.

If the inductive effect of the heteroatom outweighs the conjugation effect into the carbonyl group, the carbonyl stretching frequency is higher than 1710 cm^{-1}.

16. B is correct.

The various peaks between 900 and 1500 cm^{-1} correspond to the unique fingerprint region in the IR spectrum.

The prominent peak at 1710 cm^{-1} indicates the carbon-oxygen double bond of a carbonyl (C=O) group (aldehyde, ketone, acyl halide, anhydride, carboxylic acid, ester, or amide).

A similar (prominent and broad peak) between 3300 and 3500 cm^{-1} is characteristic of alcohol.

The alcohol of a carboxylic acid would show an IR absorption peak around 2800 and 3200 cm^{-1}.

17. B is correct.

Spectroscopy (e.g., NMR) generally is used in the identification of compounds.

Distillation, crystallization, and extraction are common techniques to isolate and purify compounds.

18. C is correct.

For carboxylic acid derivatives, the heteroatom either increases or decreases the stretching frequency of the carbonyl group.

If the lone pair conjugation with the carbonyl is the more dominant effect (e.g., amides), the carbonyl stretching frequency is lower than 1710 cm^{-1}.

If the inductive effect of the heteroatom outweighs the conjugation effect into the carbonyl group (e.g., esters and acid chlorides), then the stretching frequency is higher than 1710 cm^{-1}.

19. A is correct.

NMR spectroscopy provides information about the local environment of the proton.

Equivalent hydrogens (i.e., hydrogens in identical locations about other atoms) produce a single NMR signal.

Nonequivalent hydrogens give separate NMR signals on the spectrum.

Since the molecule produces one signal for NMR, all hydrogens are equivalent. In $(CH_3)_3CCCl_2C(CH_3)_3$, the methyl groups are equivalent, and this molecule produces only one signal in NMR.

B: $(CH_3)_2CHCH_2CH_2CH(CH_3)CH_2CH_3$ produces eight signals. Additionally, the splitting produces a complex NMR pattern indicating the number of adjacent Hs.

C: $(CH_3)_2CHCH_2(CH_2)_4CH_3$ produces eight signals. Additionally, the splitting produces a complex NMR pattern indicating the number of adjacent Hs.

D: $CH_3(CH_2)_7CH_3$ produces five signals. For symmetrical molecules, one signal is for the terminal $CH_3(1,9)$, one for the $CH_2(2,8)$, one for the $CH_2(3,7)$, one for the $CH_2(4,6)$, and one for the CH_2 at 5.

20. A is correct.

Note: the displayed masses on the mass spectrum corresponds to molecular fragments with a charge of +1. It is possible to generate dications from the ionization in the mass spectrometer, and therefore an additional calculation may be required to determine the true mass of the fragment.

21. B is correct.

The two nuclear spin states for protons are *alpha* and *beta*.

The *alpha* spin state has less energy than the *beta* spin state because the *alpha* spin state has the same direction as the applied external field.

22. C is correct.

IR spectroscopy provides information about functional groups.

A: *mass spectrometry* (MS) provides information about molecular weight.

B: *nuclear magnetic resonance* (NMR) spectroscopy provides information about protons.

D: *UV spectroscopy* provides information about conjugated (i.e., sp^2 hybridization) double bonds.

E: *polarity* refers to the difference in electron density due to electronegative atoms.

23. A is correct.

The *fragmentation pattern* of the spectra provides structural information and determination of the molar weight of an unknown compound.

Cleavage occurs at alkyl-substituted carbons reflecting the order generally observed in carbocations.

3,3-dimethyl-2-butanone

The *base peak* for this molecule is the acetyl intermediate. This intermediate results from the ionization of the carbonyl oxygen atom to form an oxygen-centered radical cation.

The carbon-carbon bond between the *tert*-butyl group and the carbonyl can homolytically cleave to give the acylium cation.

For example:

24. C is correct.

Topicity is the stereochemical relationship between substituents.

These groups, depending on the relationship, can be *heterotopic, homotopic, enantiotopic,* or *diastereotopic.*

The protons are chemically equivalent or homotopic because the groups are equivalent.

If labeling the protons of methylene (~CH_2~) group as H_a and H_b does not form *enantiomers*, the molecule is *homotopic*.

25. A is correct.

IR active molecules must have polarized covalent bonds to absorb IR.

When a Cl–Cl bond with atoms of the same electronegativity stretches or bends, no dipole is created, and therefore the molecule is IR inactive.

B: CO (C≡O) contains covalent bonds whereby carbon is attached to the electronegative oxygen, which creates a dipole generating an IR signal.

C: $CH_3CH_2CH_2OH$ contains covalent bonds attached to an electronegative oxygen, which creates a dipole generating an IR signal.

D: CH_3Br contains covalent bonds attached to electronegative bromines, creating a dipole with an IR signal.

E: HCN contains covalent bonds attached to the electronegative nitrogen, creating a dipole with an IR signal.

26. A is correct.

Electromagnetic spectrum:

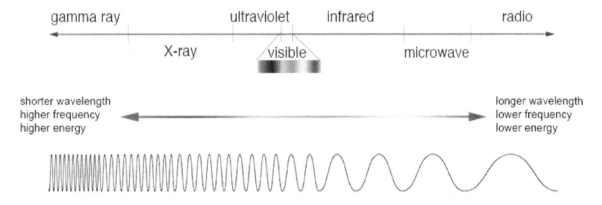

Radio waves have the lowest energy on the electromagnetic spectrum, infrared radiation has more energy than radio waves, and ultraviolet light has more energy than infrared radiation.

27. E is correct.

The type of electromagnetic radiation (EMR) needed to excite an electron in the molecule from the highest energy occupied molecular orbital (*HOMO*) to the lowest energy unoccupied molecular orbital (*LUMO*) corresponds to UV-visible light.

Exciting an electron from the *sigma* bond is more difficult because the *sigma* bond has very low energy and requires higher energy radiation to be promoted to a vacant orbital.

Furthermore, the *sigma** orbital has very high energy; promoting electrons to this vacant orbital requires stronger radiation.

28. A is correct.

UV spectroscopy is useful for identifying compounds with conjugated double bonds. Neither dimethyl ether nor bromoethane has conjugated double bonds, so UV is not a good analytical technique to distinguish them.

B: *mass spectrometry* (MS) provides information about the molecular weight, the number and size of molecular fragments, and a unique fingerprint pattern.

C: *infrared* (IR) spectroscopy determines if the molecule contains certain functional groups and gives a unique fingerprint pattern for a molecule.

D: *proton nuclear magnetic resonance* (NMR) examines the molecular environment of the hydrogens and is related to where the signal is located on the spectrum.

NMR is useful in determining the connectivity of the atoms and identifies the relative numbers of each kind of hydrogen (i.e., integration number given by the area under each signal) and the number of hydrogen atoms on adjacent atoms (i.e., splitting pattern as determined by n + 1, where n = number of adjacent Hs).

29. D is correct.

The compound is an ester. The 3.8 ppm septet corresponds to the single C–H bond near the oxygen of the ester.

The singlet at 2.2 ppm suggests that the ~CH$_3$ group is near the carbonyl group.

The doublet at 1.0 ppm corresponds to the methyl groups of the isopropyl portion of the molecule.

30. E is correct.

Conjugated polyenes absorb light at longer wavelengths than unconjugated alkenes because the additional *p* orbital overlap in larger *pi* systems decreases the energy difference between the highest occupied molecular orbital (*HOMO*) and the lowest unoccupied molecular orbital (*LUMO*).

The *LUMO* is an antibonding orbital and has more energy than the *HOMO*, a bonding orbital.

The longer the conjugated system, the smaller the energy gap between the two molecular orbitals (MO); this requires radiation of less energy (and longer wavelength) for electron transitions.

When a molecule absorbs UV/visible radiation, electrons are promoted from one orbital to a higher energy orbital.

31. B is correct.

For NMR, the position that hydrogen absorbs is determined by the chemical environment.

If the chemical environment of two hydrogens is identical, only one signal is produced.

Therefore, equivalent hydrogens could be replaced by another group to yield the same molecule.

The challenge is in determining whether hydrogens are in identical environments (i.e., symmetric molecules).

1,2-dibromoethane has one absorbance for the NMR spectrum because a molecule has one type of H atom.

A: *tert*-butyl alcohol produces 2 signals.

C: *toluene* produces 2 signals.

D: *methanol* produces 2 signals.

E: *phenol* produces 4 signals.

32. A is correct.

IR absorption between 1630 cm^{-1} and 1740 cm^{-1} is characteristic of carbonyls (e.g., aldehydes, ketones, anhydrides, carboxylic acids, esters, and amides).

An IR absorption of 1735 cm^{-1} is characteristic of an ester.

33. D is correct.

UV light has enough energy to excite electrons to higher energy vacant orbitals as photoactivated atoms.

This radiation generally is not strong enough to eject electrons from atoms of most elements to form ions.

34. B is correct.

Infrared radiation (IR) is useful in 1500 to 3500 cm^{-1} (called wavenumbers). In this range, the molecular vibrations of molecules are active, and characteristic absorbance frequencies identify functional groups.

Below 1500 cm^{-1} is the fingerprint region used for more detailed analysis once the target molecule(s) have been identified.

A: *nuclear magnetic resonance* (NMR) spectroscopy involves a sample containing the compound being subjected to a high-intensity magnetic field and scanning through the radio-frequency range of the electromagnetic spectrum for particular absorptions.

NMR relies on the magnetic properties of specific atomic nuclei and determines the physical and chemical properties of atoms within molecules. NMR can be used to deduce the structure (connectivity) of the atoms within the molecule.

C: the *UV range* (not the IR range) of wavelengths is between 200–400 nm and corresponds to the energy required for electronic transitions between the bonding or nonbonding molecular orbitals and antibonding molecular orbitals.

continued…

UV spectroscopy is useful for studying compounds with double bonds, especially in conjugated (i.e., alternating double and single bond) molecules.

When molecules containing π-electrons (or non-bonding electrons) absorb UV energy, these electrons are promoted (i.e., excited) to higher antibonding molecular orbitals.

The more easily excited the electrons (i.e., lower energy gap between the *HOMO* and the *LUMO*), the longer the wavelength of UV light it absorbs.

D: *mass spectrometry* (MS) studies compounds through the fragmentation of molecules, although the unfragmented parent peak provides useful information.

Note: mass spectrometry destroys (fragments) the sample and is not preferred for rare/limited samples.

35. B is correct.

The IR absorbance at 1710 cm^{-1} indicates the carbonyl group of a ketone or an aldehyde.

The carbonyl (C=O) is present in the derivatives of carboxylic acid: acyl halide, anhydride, carboxylic acid, esters, and amide.

NMR can distinguish between an aldehyde (NMR δ 9–10) and a ketone (no characteristic NMR signals).

Aldehydes have additional peaks at 2700–2800 cm^{-1}, while ketones do not.

36. B is correct.

The broad, deep absorption between 3000 cm^{-1} to 3500 cm^{-1} is characteristic for alcohol (~OH).

The carbonyl (C=O) is also present in carboxylic acid derivatives: acyl halide, anhydride, carboxylic acid, esters, and amide.

NMR distinguishes between an aldehyde (NMR δ 9–10) and a ketone (no characteristic NMR signals).

Aldehydes have additional peaks at 2700–2800 cm^{-1}, while ketones do not.

Notes for active learning

Notes for active learning

Alkanes and Alkyl Halides – Detailed Explanations

1. C is correct.

A nucleophile donates lone pairs of electrons; therefore, it is a Lewis base.

2. D is correct.

 There are three tertiary alkyl positions (i.e., carbon bonded to three other carbons).

3. B is correct.

S_N2 is bimolecular; rate = k [substrate] × [nucleophile].

Therefore, if the nucleophile ($^-$OH) concentration is doubled, then the reaction rate doubles.

Since the alkyl halide is primary, a unimolecular (S_N1) reaction occurs.

Water stabilizes the carbocation intermediate and thereby increases the rate of the reaction.

4. D is correct.

Only the electrophile concentration controls the reaction rate because the rate-determining step is the unimolecular formation of the carbocation.

S_N1 reactions proceed *via* a carbocation in the first step of the mechanism.

In the second step, the nucleophile forms a new bond by attacking the carbocation.

S_N1 undergoes first-order kinetics, whereby:

$$rate = k[substrate]$$

5. E is correct.

Alkanes are only composed of hydrogen and carbon atoms. Because the electronegativity of these atoms is quite similar, large bond dipoles are not expected.

Hydrogen bonding is a force that acts through highly polarized bonds to form intermolecular bonds to partial positive hydrogen atoms (H attached to F, O or N).

6. A is correct.

The sodium methoxide in this reaction acts as a strong base and abstracts a proton on the carbon atom that neighbors the chloride. The mechanism for this process is E_2.

The reaction is not S_N1 because heat is needed to generate the carbocation, not included in the rxn conditions.

7. B is correct. The order of stability of carbocations is $3° > 2° > 1°$.

Therefore, more substituted carbocations are more stable.

8. D is correct.

1-bromopropane is a primary halogen and a strong nucleophile, leading to S_N2, preferred without steric hindrance.

9. C is correct.

Molecules with double or triple bonds cannot undergo free rotation because the *pi* bond rigidifies the structure of the compound. To achieve the bond rotation, the *pi* bond(s) must be broken.

Furthermore, for cyclic compounds, the smaller the ring size, the fewer degrees of freedom it has.

Due to strain energy, cyclopropane is unable to rotate freely.

10. B is correct.

The concentration of substrate and nucleophile control the reaction rate because the rate-determining step is bimolecular.

S_N2 undergoes *second-order kinetics* whereby:

$$\text{rate} = k \, [\text{substrate}] \times [\text{nucleophile}]$$

11. D is correct.

The heat of combustion (ΔH_c°) is the energy released (as heat) when a compound undergoes complete combustion with oxygen.

The chemical reaction is typically a hydrocarbon reacting with oxygen to form carbon dioxide, water, and heat. General formula:

$$C_nH_{2n+2} + ((3n+1)/2)O_2 \rightarrow (n+1)H_2O + nCO_2 + \text{energy}$$

The heat of combustion of a compound depends on three main factors: molecular weight, angle strain, and degree of branching.

In most cases, the compound with a higher molecular weight (i.e., more C–C and C–H bonds) has the larger heat of combustion.

For straight-chain alkanes, each addition of methylene ($\sim CH_2\sim$) groups adds approximately –157 kcal/mole to the heat of combustion.

For cycloalkanes, the heat of combustion increases with increasing angle strain.

Reference: 1 kJ·mol^{-1} is equal to $0.239 \text{ kcal·mol}^{-1}$

ΔH_c° for alkanes increase by about 657 kJ/mol (157 kcal/mol) per $\sim CH_2\sim$ group.

For example, heptane has 4 more $\sim CH_2\sim$ groups than propane:

$$4 \times -157 \text{ kcal per mole} = -628 \text{ kcal/mol}$$

Yields:

$$-530 \text{ (propane)} + -628 = -1{,}094 \text{ kcal/mol (heptane)}$$

12. D is correct.

Identify the molecules that contain nitrogen or oxygen heteroatoms because these atoms enable molecules to participate in hydrogen bonding and contribute to dipolar interactions.

Cyclopentane is only composed of hydrogen and carbon, so it is the least water-soluble.

13. D is correct.

Unimolecular elimination occurs *via* E_1 and forms a carbocation in the slow (rate-determining) step.

A: a single step (concerted) process describes bimolecular (E_2), not E_1 elimination.

B: homolytic (compared to the more common heterolytic) cleavage of a covalent bond yields free radicals.

C: free radicals occur with peroxides (H_2O_2) or dihalides / UV, and radicals are an intermediate in unimolecular (E_1) elimination.

14. C is correct.

Since an S_N1 reaction proceeds through a planar, sp^2 hybridized carbocation intermediate (which can be attacked from either side), it forms a racemic mixture (i.e., both R / S stereoisomers are present).

15. B is correct.

S_N1 reactions favor substituted alkyl halides because of the stability of the carbocation intermediates, whereas S_N2 reactions favor unsubstituted reactants due to minimal steric hindrance for the approaching nucleophile.

A: S_N1 reaction rates are greatly affected by electronic factors (degree of substitution and inductive influence of electronegative atoms), while S_N2 reaction rates are greatly affected by steric (hindrance) factors.

C: S_N1 reactions proceed *via* a carbocation intermediate, but S_N2 reactions (*bimolecular*) proceed *via* a single-step reaction involving a concerted mechanism with a transition state instead of a carbocation.

D: S_N2 reactions are bimolecular reactions that proceed *via* a single-step reaction with a transition state (i.e., bond making and breaking events) rather than *via* an intermediate.

E: S_N2 reactions are favored by polar aprotic solvents (i.e., cannot dissociate a proton into the solution), such as THF, DMSO, EtOAc, which do not stabilize the strong (i.e., negatively charged anion) nucleophile, so it remains more reactive to drive the bimolecular reaction of S_N2.

S_N1 reactions proceed *via* polar protic solvents (e.g., H_2O, methanol), which tend to stabilize the carbocation (positive charge) by electrostatic attraction to the resulting anion of the dissociated solvent.

16. D is correct.

Structural isomers have the same molecular formula (C_7H_{16}) but different atomic connections.

Molecular mass would be a consideration if the molecules were not isomers (same molecular formula).

Branching in alkanes lowers the boiling point because branched molecules cannot interact as effectively as unbranched molecules and have less surface area. 2,2,4-trimethylpentane has the lowest boiling point because it is the most highly branched.

Hydrogen bonding is a strong attractive force between molecules (intermolecular force) but requires hydrogen to be attached to an electronegative atom (fluorine, oxygen, or nitrogen).

The next most attractive intermolecular force is dipole-dipole interaction.

17. D is correct.

S_N2 reactions are concerted reactions with a single step and do not form charged intermediates.

Carbocation intermediates are a feature of S_N1 and E_1 mechanisms.

18. B is correct.

The twist-boat is located at a local energy minimum (or trough) for the conformers of cyclohexane.

Relative energy diagram for conformers (i.e., chair flips) of cyclohexane

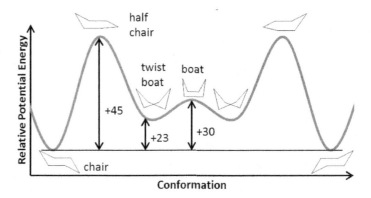

19. B is correct.

To form propyl chloride, one of six hydrogens (3 on each methyl group) can be substituted. To form isopropyl chloride, the hydrogen extracted must be one of the two on the middle carbon.

Based on statistical probability, propyl chloride forms in a 3:1 ratio compared to isopropyl chloride.

When terminal hydrogen is extracted (to form propyl chloride), a primary radical intermediate is formed; when internal hydrogen is extracted (to form isopropyl chloride), a secondary radical intermediate forms.

Carbon radicals are electron-deficient because they do not have a full octet.

Alkyl groups are electron-donating (*via* hyperconjugation), so a secondary radical is more stable than a primary radical, and therefore the formation of a secondary radical is more likely.

The reaction proceeding through the secondary radical intermediate is faster. Therefore, the reaction leading to the formation of isopropyl chloride proceeds more readily. This is contrary to strictly statistical considerations, and more isopropyl chloride is formed than the predicted 25%.

Note: it is impossible to predict what percentages form because other factors, such as temperature, are important for the empirical yield determination for each product.

20. D is correct.

S_N1 reactions proceed *via* a carbocation in the first step of the mechanism.

In the second step, the nucleophile forms a new bond by attacking the carbocation.

S_N1 undergoes first-order kinetics, whereby:

rate = k[substrate]

where k is a rate constant determined experimentally.

21. C is correct.

Conformations in which the single bonds are staggered are more stable than those in which they are eclipsed due to steric repulsion and torsional strain (i.e., bonding electron between adjacent atoms – such as observed in eclipsed Newman projections).

Torsional strain is present in Newman projections when the substituents are eclipsed. It originates from the repulsion of the bonding electrons (i.e., not the steric interactions of the substituents).

Conformations that put the largest substituents in an *anti* (180° offset) arrangement are more stable than those in a *gauche* (60° offset) arrangement.

1,2-dibromoethane shown anti in the Newman projection

22. D is correct.

S_N2 reactions are favored with primary substrates, strong nucleophiles, good leaving groups, and polar aprotic solvents. 1-bromobutane is a primary alkyl halide, ⁻CN is an extremely strong nucleophile, and bromine is a good leaving group.

S_N2 occurs exclusively over elimination E_2 because ⁻CN is a strong, linear nucleophile; ⁻CN is not sterically hindered as a base.

Only when strong, bulky bases (e.g., *tert*-butoxide) are used, elimination (e.g., E_2) is favored over substitution (e.g., S_N2).

S_N1 and E_1 reaction mechanisms are not favored with primary alkyl halides because a primary carbocation is unstable.

23. B is correct.

S_N1 proceeds when the substrate forms a carbocation.

Iodide is the best leaving group (i.e., most stable anion) and forms the cation the fastest.

24. C is correct.

Acetate anion

Dimethyl sulfoxide (DMSO) is an organosulfur compound with the formula $(CH_3)_2SO$.

$$H_3C-\overset{\overset{O}{\|}}{S}-CH_3$$

The colorless liquid is an important polar aprotic solvent that dissolves polar and nonpolar compounds and is miscible with water and a wide range of organic solvents.

25. C is correct.

Strong nucleophiles have a negative formal charge (i.e., lone pairs excess), while weak nucleophiles are neutral species with a lone pair of electrons.

26. A is correct.

E_1 is a unimolecular elimination that proceeds *via* a carbocation intermediate in a two-step reaction.

Substitution of the substrate (3° > 2° > 1° >> methyl) increases the rate of E_1 (and S_N1) reactions because highly branched carbon chains (with more substituted carbons) form more stable carbocations.

S_N2 is a bimolecular nucleophilic substitution that proceeds *via* a one-step (concerted mechanisms) displacement of a leaving group by a nucleophile.

S_N2 is favored by unbranched carbon chains because the nucleophilic displacement of a leaving group by a nucleophile is favored due to less steric hindrance.

Secondary carbons could undergo both E_1 and S_N2. The cyanide group is a very poor leaving group because it is an unstable anion and is unlikely to dissociate *via* E_1 or be displaced *via* S_N2.

Br^- forms a stable anion and can dissociate *via* E_1 or be displaced by S_N2.

B: $(CH_3CH_2CH_2)_3CBr$ is a tertiary alkyl halide and is not favored.

C: $(CH_3CH_2CH_2)_3CCH_2Cl$ is a primary alkyl halide that lacks β-hydrogens and therefore cannot form a double bond by elimination (E_1 or E_2).

D: $(CH_3CH_2CH_2)_2CHCN$ has the leaving group (cyanide) bonded to a secondary carbon.

E: $CH_3CH_2CH_2CH_2Br$ has the leaving group (bromine) bonded to a primary carbon.

27. D is correct.

Boiling requires the molecules in the liquid phase to overcome the attractive intermolecular forces (e.g., hydrogen bonding, dipole-dipole & London dispersion forces) and move into the gas phase.

continued…

The stronger these interactions are, the more energy (i.e., heat) is needed for the molecules to separate from their neighbors and migrate into the gaseous state.

Molecules have lower boiling points when branching increases because branching disrupts the spatial packing of molecules in the solid and liquid phase, and therefore branching reduces intermolecular attractions.

A: *cis*-2-pentene has a slightly higher boiling point because unsaturation establishes a dipole moment that raises their relative boiling point compared to alkanes.

B: 2-pentyne has a slightly higher boiling point because unsaturation establishes a dipole moment that raises their relative boiling point compared with alkanes.

C: pentane is a hydrocarbon and only experiences weak London dispersion forces.

E: 3-pentanol exhibits hydrogen bonding and has a relatively high boiling point compared with molecules of comparable molecular weight that lack hydrogen bonding.

28. C is correct.

A *trans* isomer requires that the substituents point in opposite directions (up and down).

Therefore, one substituent is located axial, while the other substituent is equatorial.

In this substituted cyclohexane, the molecule is more stable when the larger substituents are equatorial.

When comparing methyl and isopropyl, the isopropyl is larger and therefore is located equatorially.

29. A is correct.

E_1 and S_N1 reactions are strongly favored by highly branched carbon chains and good leaving groups.

E_2 reactions are largely independent of the structure of carbon chains and are favored by good leaving groups, which can easily be eliminated by basic conditions.

S_N2 reactions are strongly favored by substrates with unbranched carbon chains.

$(CH_3CH_2CH_2)_3CBr$ is a tertiary alkyl halide.

B: $CH_3CH_2CH_2CH_3$ is a hydrocarbon where alkanes do not undergo elimination or nucleophilic substitution. Alkanes are unreactive to most organic chemistry reagents and can either undergo combustion (i.e., burning of propane) or free radical halogenation to introduce a halogen as a leaving group.

C: $(CH_3CH_2)_3COH$ is a highly branched tertiary alcohol carbon chain, so it cannot undergo an S_N2 reaction. Also, ^-OH is a very poor leaving group, so it does not readily undergo substitution. With heat, alcohols undergo elimination *via* dehydration (i.e., removal of water).

D: $CH_3CH_2CH_2CH_2Br$ is a primary alkyl halide that undergoes S_N2 and E_2, but neither S_N1 nor E_1.

30. A is correct.

In a complete combustion reaction, a compound reacts with an oxidizing element (e.g., oxygen), and the products are compounds of each element in the fuel combined with the oxidizing element.

General formula:

$$C_nH_{2n+2} + [(3n + 1) / 2]O_2 \rightarrow (n +1)H_2O + nCO_2 + energy$$

For example, methane yields:

$$CH_4 + 2\ O_2 \rightarrow CO_2 + 2\ H_2O + energy$$

Nonane:

$$C_9H_{20} + [(3 \times 9 + 1) / 2]O_2 \rightarrow (9 + 1)H_2O + 9\ CO_2 + energy$$

$$C_9H_{20} + 14\ O_2 \rightarrow 10\ H_2O + 9\ CO_2 + energy$$

Since nonane has the molecular formula C_9H_{20}, the combustion of 1 mole of neopentane produces 9 moles of CO_2 and 10 moles of H_2O.

31. D is correct.

Free radical halogenation is a few reactions (along with combustion) that alkanes undergo and occur *via* a highly reactive halogen radical.

A radical is a single, neutrally charged atom with an unhybridized *p* orbital with a single unpaired electron that causes it to be reactive.

Steps for free radical halogenation:

Step I: initiation forms the free radical from a diatomic molecule (X_2) by homolytic bond cleavage. Initiation is shown in the first reaction equation and is usually catalyzed by ultraviolet light ($h\nu$), heat, or by an attack by another free radical.

Step II: propagation involves a radical and a neutral molecule, and the products are a new neutral molecule and a new radical. The halogen-free radical attacks the neutral alkane and, *via* homolytic bond cleavage, produces a new H–X bond and another highly reactive free radical as the alkyl radical.

The alkyl radical reacts with Br_2 to form the alkyl halide and another halogen radical. This new halogen radical then starts the process again, thus causing a chain reaction (propagation).

Step III: termination joins the two radicals. For example, an alkyl radical attacks a halogen radical to produce a new neutral molecule.

I: $Br_2 + h\nu \rightarrow 2\ Br\bullet$ is UV light-induced generation of two free radicals and is the chain initiating step.

II: $Br\bullet + RH \rightarrow HBr + R\bullet$ is a chain propagating step because the reaction advances the chain onward by generating a new neutral product plus a new free radical.

III: $R\bullet + Br_2 \rightarrow RBr + Br\bullet$ is a chain propagating step because the reaction advances the chain onward by generating a new neutral product plus a new free radical.

32. B is correct.

As a concerted mechanism, the single step of the S_N2 reaction is a simultaneous substitution occurring with the formation of a new bond while the original bond breaks.

S_N2 undergoes second-order kinetics.

rate = k [substrate] × [nucleophile]

33. A is correct.

Alkanes undergo free radical halogenation to substitute a C–H bond with a C–X bond, where X is a halogen.

Alkenes and alkynes generally undergo addition reactions instead, where an electrophile may add across a carbon-carbon *pi* bond.

34. B is correct.

Bimolecular nucleophilic substitution (S_N2) occurs at the fastest rate when the substrate is the least hindered.

The relative reactivity of the alkyl halides for S_N2 is methyl > primary > secondary >> tertiary.

S_N2 reactions do not occur on sterically hindered tertiary substrates.

A: 1-chloro-2,2-diethylcyclopentane is a secondary alkyl halide.

This substrate does not undergo S_N2 substitution as rapidly as 1-chlorocyclopentane because branching adjacent to the carbon-containing leaving group reduces the rate of S_N2 reactions since the approach of the nucleophile is impeded compared to a straight-chain molecule.

C: 1-chlorocyclopentene does not undergo nucleophilic substitution because it has a halogen attached to a vinylic (i.e., on a double bond) carbon.

D: 1-chloro-1-ethylcyclopentane is a tertiary halide and does not undergo S_N2 nucleophilic substitution.

The mechanism is S_N1 (with a carbocation intermediate).

E: *tert*-butylchloride is a tertiary halide and does not undergo S_N2 nucleophilic substitution.

The mechanism is S_N1 (with a carbocation intermediate).

35. D is correct.

Stable molecules are the best leaving groups.

If the leaving groups are charged, then the bromide ion is the best leaving group because the anion is stable (due to atomic size).

The order of the halogens as leaving groups: $I^- > Br^- > Cl^- > F^-$

The order of the halogens as nucleophiles: $I^- > Br^- > Cl^- > F^-$

36. E is correct.

Radical termination steps involve an overall decrease in the number of radicals when comparing the starting materials to the products.

The correct answer involves a decrease in the number of radicals (from two to zero).

A: the number of radicals increases from zero to two, which is an initiation step.

B: the number of radicals (one) does not change, which are propagation steps.

C and D: the number of radicals (one) does not change, which are propagation steps.

E: the number of radicals decreases from two to zero, which is a termination step.

Notes for active learning

Notes for active learning

Alkenes – Detailed Explanations

1. C is correct.

Although these reactions produce the same products and in the same quantities, what is different is the rate of the borane addition for each alkene.

(*E*)-3-heptene

(*Z*)-3-hexene

The *E* has the highest priority substituents on opposite sides, while the *Z* alkene has the alkyl substituents on the same side.

Therefore, because *Z* alkenes are less thermodynamically stable than *E* alkenes, *Z* alkenes are more reactive.

Furthermore, the approach of the borane to the *Z* alkene is less sterically demanding because the *Z* alkene is more open to an attack (alkyl groups are on the same side).

2. B is correct.

The addition of deuterium (an isotope of hydrogen) across a C=C double bond is metal-catalyzed. It proceeds with *syn* stereoselectivity, adding both deuterium to the same face of the double bond.

3. D is correct.

The trapping of mercury-alkene cations typically opens on the more substituted side, but the *tert*-butyl group sufficiently blocks access to this side. Therefore, the cation is opened on the more terminal side.

4. D is correct.

HI is the strongest acid of the given molecules, so it protonates the fastest (followed by HBr, then HCl).

Also, I⁻ is the best nucleophile, so it adds to the carbocation most rapidly.

5. D is correct.

In 1,3-butadiene, C–2 and C–3 are sp^2 hybridized with unhybridized *p* orbitals involved in π bonding. The bond between C–2 and C–3 results from the overlap of two sp^2 hybridized orbitals.

There cannot be a partial double-bond character due to σ electrons; double bonds result only from π electrons.

6. A is correct.

In the first step of the reaction, the H$^+$ adds to the double bond creating a carbocation.

The nucleophilic water attacks the carbocation, and the acid is regenerated in the last step of the reaction.

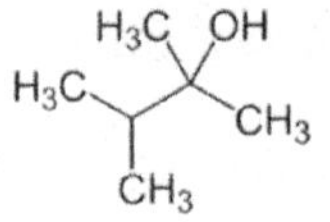

2,3-dimethyl-2-butanol

7. A is correct.

The rate law may not reveal the steps in a reaction mechanism.

Furthermore, the bromination of alkenes proceeds in two steps, not one.

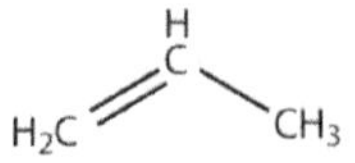

8. D is correct.

Draw the structures of the starting material and product.

Two halogen atoms are added to the molecule, and an efficient method to achieve this is by exposing the alkene to a diatomic halogen species (e.g., Cl$_2$ or Br$_2$).

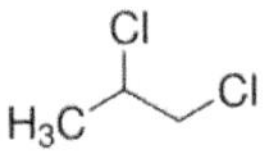

The chlorine atoms add in an *anti*-orientation from the 3-membered ring of the chloronium ion.

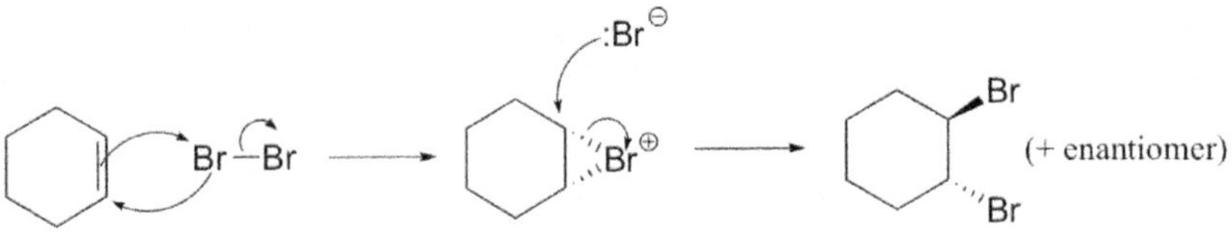

bromoniom ion

Bromonium (like chloronium) ions undergo the same reaction mechanism.

9. A is correct.

The Zaitsev product is the most thermodynamically stable.

Thermodynamically stable alkenes are most substituted (3° > 2° > 1°).

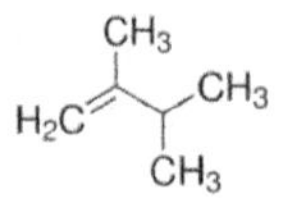

2,3-dimethyl-1-butene has a 1° alkene carbon (terminal) and a 3° carbon (at position 2).

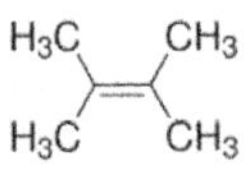

2,3-dimethyl-2-butene has two 3° alkene carbons at positions 2 and 3.

Hyperconjugation of the neighboring C–H bonds into the *pi** orbital of the alkene lowers the alkene's energy.

Furthermore, the *sp*^{3} hybridized alkyl groups help to inductively donate electron density to the more electronegative *sp*^{2} hybridized carbon atoms.

10. C is correct.

Conjugation is the alternation of double and single bonds, which results in the delocalization of electrons *via* resonance through the sp^2 hybridized carbons, resulting in increased stability for the molecule.

1,3,5-heptatriene has three conjugated double (π) bonds.

A: 1,2-hexadiene has two cumulated, rather than conjugated, π bonds.

Cumulated molecules have a *sp* carbon in the center of the two double bonds – this is unstable and increases the overall energy of the molecule.

B: 1,3-hexadiene has two conjugated double bonds.

D: 1,5-hexadiene has two isolated π bonds.

E: 1,2,3-heptatriene is cumulated. Cumulated molecules have a *sp* carbon in the center of the two double bonds – this is unstable and increases the overall energy of the molecule.

11. A is correct.

Water, methanol, and acetic acid are poor solvents because they can react as nucleophiles and add to alkenes.

12. C is correct.

The hydration proceeds with Markovnikov addition.

The first step in the reaction is protonation to form the tertiary carbocation trapped by water.

13. A is correct.

A conjugated system has two or more double or triple bonds separated by a single bond (i.e., sp^2 hybridization at each carbon in the conjugated system).

1,2-butadiene is not conjugated because the double bonds are adjacent (not separated by a single bond). Adjacent double bonds are cumulated and are unstable.

B: cyclobutadiene is conjugated because the molecule has two double bonds separated by single bonds.

C: benzene is conjugated because a single bond separates each double bond.

D: 1,3-cyclohexadiene is conjugated because a single bond separates the double bonds between carbons 1-2 and carbons 3-4.

E: 2,4-pentadiene is conjugated because the molecule has two double bonds separated by a single bond.

14. A is correct.

In $(CH_3)_2C=C(CH_3)CH_2CH_3$, both carbons of the alkene are equally substituted (i.e., tertiary), so the two putative carbocations are approximately equally stable.

The addition of a hydrogen halide across a double bond can create two chiral centers, one at each of the former sp^2 carbons. The carbocation forms preferentially at the more substituted carbon.

15. C is correct. Oxymercuration-reduction of an alkene yields Markovnikov orientation and *anti*-addition.

By comparison, hydroboration-oxidation of an alkene is consistent with *anti*-Markovnikov and *syn* addition.

Step one uses BH_3 to add BH_2 and H as *syn* addition across the double bond of the alkene.

Step two uses peroxides and nucleophilic oxygen for *syn* addition of a hydroxyl. Other nucleophiles (e.g., methanol) can add *syn* addition as an ether substituent across the double bond.

16. D is correct.

Geometric isomers have the same molecular formula but different connectivity between the atoms due to the orientation of substituents around a carbon-carbon double bond (or ring).

In *cis* isomers, the same substituents are on one side of the double bond or ring, while in *trans* isomers, the same substituents are on opposite sides of the double bond or ring.

Isomers (same molecular formula, but different molecules) with no double bonds cannot be geometric isomers.

Isomers include:

Constitutional isomers – different connectivity of the backbone or containing different functional groups;

Enantiomers – mirror images of chiral molecules;

Diastereomers – non-mirror chiral molecules with 2 or more chiral centers or geometric isomers containing double bonds (i.e., designated as *cis/trans* or *E/Z*).

17. A is correct.

The methyl group adjacent to the carbocation migrates *via* a methide shift to give a tertiary carbocation, which then loses a proton to form the most substituted alkene (i.e., both carbons of the alkene are tertiary).

18. B is correct.

The reaction conditions are for the halohydration of an alkene. The bromonium ion forms first; this is attacked (ring opens) by water as a nucleophile on the more substituted side.

19. D is correct.

A *bromonium ion* is a cyclic (three-membered ring) structure of a bromine atom attached to two unsaturated carbons (i.e., an alkene).

The bromonium ion is formed when the nucleophilic double bond adds to a bromine atom of Br_2, releasing Br^-.

The resulting bromine anion (or solvent if it is a nucleophile – contains lone pairs of electrons: H_2O, NH_3 or CH_3OH) bonds to the more substituted carbon of the bromonium structure dibrominated product. Cl_2 follows the same reaction mechanism.

An *anti*-product is formed because the Br^- (or nucleophilic solvent with lone pairs) must approach the three-membered ring of the bromonium ion from the side opposite the bromonium ion.

$CH_3CH_2CH=CH_2 + HBr \rightarrow CH_3CH_2CHBrCH_3$: HBr adds to alkenes *via* a Markovnikov mechanism. The double bond attacks the proton, and hydrogen adds to the carbon of the double bond with fewer alkyl substituents (i.e., less substituted carbon).

As a result, a carbocation intermediate forms on the more substituted carbon.

Second, Br^- adds to the carbocation (more substituted carbon) to form the alkyl halide. The mechanism involves a carbocation and not a bromonium ion.

Unlike a bromonium ion, which yields the *anti*-stereochemistry, the trigonal planar carbocation undergoes nucleophilic attack from either face (e.g., the top and bottom). It produces enantiomers (a racemic mixture) if the product contains a chiral center on the carbocation carbon.

20. C is correct.

cis-3-methyl-2-hexene undergoes Markovnikov addition because the first step is protonation to give the more stable (more substituted) carbonium ion. It gives *syn*- and *anti*-addition products because, in the second step, the bromide ion attacks the top and bottom faces of the carbonium ion.

Adding a hydrogen halide to an asymmetrical alkene leads to either halogenated alkene. The halide is on the more substituted carbon or a product in which the halide is on the less substituted carbon.

The former addition follows Markovnikov's rule, and the latter is an example of an *anti*-Markovnikov addition. If a mixture of the two products is formed, with a predominance of one product, the reaction is *regioselective*.

21. E is correct.

Addition reactions require two or more reagents to combine to form a single product.

For the oxidation of an alkene (e.g., epoxidation or dihydroxylation), only the oxygen atoms of a reagent are transferred to the alkene. A reagent byproduct is typically given off in the reaction, such as the carboxylic acid from *m*CPBA oxidation (i.e., peroxyacid) or the reduced metal from potassium permanganate ($KMnO_4$) or osmium tetraoxide (OsO_4) oxidation.

Ozonolysis (O_3 or Cr_2O_7) is a type of oxidation of alkenes splitting the alkene into two separate carbonyl-containing products (i.e., cleavage reaction) and is not an addition reaction.

22. A is correct.

Hydrogen bromide will not substitute an alkane because alkanes are unreactive. Alkanes undergo substitution only under extreme conditions (e.g., *hv* as UV light) or yield combustion products CO_2 and H_2O.

N-bromosuccinimide (NBS) adds bromine to the allylic position (i.e., one away from a double bond). The product is: butene + NBS → 3-bromobutene

Reaction 2: at high temperatures, alkanes undergo combustion to form CO_2 and H_2O.

Reaction 3: free radical substitution is initiated for highly reactive free radicals (e.g., Br_2 or Cl_2), with Br_2 being more selective, whereby the Br radical adds to the more substituted carbon of the alkene.

Reaction 4: Br_2 in CCl_4 adds bromines to an alkene as a bromonium intermediate, with the second bromide adding to the more substituted carbon of the alkene.

23. C is correct.

Use the following formulae to calculate the *degrees of unsaturation*:

   C_nH_{2n+2}: for an alkane (0 degrees of unsaturation)

   C_nH_{2n}: for an alkene or a ring (1 degree of unsaturation)

   C_nH_{2n-2}: for an alkyne, 2 double bonds, 2 rings or 1 ring and 1 double bond (2 degrees of unsaturation)

There are two degrees of unsaturation for the compound C_6H_{10}.

24. C is correct.

Conjugated (alternating double and single) bonds are more thermodynamically stable than unconjugated double bonds.

B: adjacent double bonds of allenes are not conjugated but cumulated because the *pi* bonds are oriented 90 degrees apart. Allenes tend to be less stable, especially when confined to cyclic structures.

The other structures are isolated double bonds with (one or more) intervening sp^3 hybridized carbons between the sp^2 carbons of the double bonds.

25. A is correct.

Product A is an example of Markovnikov addition, whereby the hydrogen adds to the least substituted carbon because the most stable carbocation is formed. The bromine then adds to the (most stable) carbocation. In this example, the hydrogen adds to the secondary carbon, and the bromine adds to the tertiary carbon.

Product B involves free radical intermediates because of the hydrogen peroxide (H_2O_2).

Hydrogen peroxide causes the reaction to proceed *via* a radical intermediate (not carbocation), and the regiochemistry (where the substituents add) is *anti*-Markovnikov. The bromine adds to the least substituted carbon, and the H adds to the most substituted carbon radical.

Product C yields 2-methyl-2-butanol, according to Markovnikov addition.

26. A is correct.

Vinyl refers to an atom attached to carbon on a double bond.

Allylic refers to an atom attached to a carbon adjacent (β) to the double bond.

The chlorine substituent is directly attached to the alkene carbon atoms in vinyl chloride.

27. E is correct.

An *anti*-Markovnikov addition of water across the alkene double bond is needed.

Peroxides (H_2O_2) are a characteristic reagent for *anti*-Markovnikov regiospecificity.

28. D is correct.

Carbon-carbon *pi* bonds are elements of unsaturation, and unsaturated compounds can be reduced to give more reduced molecules (e.g., alkanes).

Alkenes have a higher oxidation state than the alkane and are equivalent to a C–O or C–X bond, where X is a more electronegative atom.

29. A is correct.

An *alkoxide* is the conjugate base of an alcohol and therefore consists of an organic moiety (i.e., group) bonded to a deprotonated (i.e., negatively charged) oxygen atom.

Secondary halides undergo bimolecular elimination (E_2) with strong bases, especially hindered ones like potassium *tert*-butoxide, $KOC(CH_3)_3$.

B: E_1 designates unimolecular elimination, generally observed in protic (i.e., H^+ donating) solvents (e.g., water or alcohols) and not when subjected to a strong alkoxide base.

C: S_N2 designates bimolecular nucleophilic substitution.

D: S_N1 designates unimolecular nucleophilic substitution.

30. B is correct.

The bromine adds to the internal position of the epoxide because the partial positive charge is greater at the more substituted position. The mechanism follows *anti*-addition stereochemistry and would be shown in the final product if the alcohol and halogen were attached to chiral carbons.

31. B is correct.

Protonation of the alkene forms the more stabilized carbocation and this cation forms at the secondary alkyl position. The cation is then trapped by water to form the alcohol.

32. A is correct.

The reaction shown is an acid-catalyzed dehydration reaction.

Alcohol in sulfuric acid and heat is characteristic of the E_1 mechanism to form an alkene.

The generated cation undergoes a ring expansion to give a more stable tertiary carbocation, which is eliminated to form the tertiary (i.e., trisubstituted) alkene.

From the rearranged carbocation, the alpha proton is eliminated by the conjugate base HSO_4^- to regenerate the sulfuric acid.

The ring (i.e., bond angle or Baeyer) strain energy drives ring expansion.

33. A is correct.

Alkanes and alkenes have *sigma* bonds.

The *pi* (i.e., double) bond in the alkenes stabilize a negative charge (as an anion) and, therefore, are more acidic.

The increased *s* character on the hybridization of an sp^2 orbital of an alkene ($pK_a = 45$) allows the orbital to accommodate the negative charge with more stability than the sp^3 of an alkane ($pK_a = 50$).

Furthermore, the increased *s* character on the hybridization of an sp orbital of an alkyne ($pK_a = 28$) allows the orbital to accommodate the negative charge with more stability than the sp^2 of an alkene.

34. A is correct.

Tertiary alkyl halides form alkenes with strong bases *via* E_2, such as sodium ethoxide ($NaOCH_2CH_3$).

The most substituted alkene is the major (Zaitsev) product that is internal or more substituted.

The least substituted alkene is the minor (Hofmann) product that is terminal or less substituted.

B: 2-methylpent-3-ene is a molecule whereby the alkene does not connect carbon with the bromine or adjacent carbon. Rearrangement does not occur in E_2 reactions because rearrangement requires a carbocation (S_N1 or E_1) intermediate.

C: 2-methyl-2-methoxypentane is the product of substitution. Tertiary alkyl halides do not undergo substitution with Lewis bases; elimination is the mechanism for product formation.

continued…

D: 2-methylpentene is a less substituted alkene and only occurs with a bulky base (e.g., tert-butyl oxide or LDA).

E: 1-methylpentene is not the product of the reaction because the carbon structure has changed, whereby the methyl group has migrated from the second carbon to the first carbon.

Additionally, the molecule would be named 2-hexene according to the longest chain.

35. C is correct.

An *anti*-Markovnikov addition of water is needed across the alkene double bond.

The reagents are borane, followed by hydrogen peroxide and sodium hydroxide.

Comparison of Markovnikov vs anti-Markovnikov addition reactions for alkenes.

Each reaction above occurs in separate steps as indicated by the vertical separation line.

A: the product of oxymercuration-demercuration: 1) $Hg(OAc)_2$, H_2O/THF; 2) $NaBH_4$

36. A is correct.

The *Cope elimination* is an intramolecular elimination reaction that occurs when the oxygen atom of the oxide of a tertiary amine removes a proton from an adjacent position.

This results in the formation of a *syn* alkene. The reaction requires heat.

The *Cope elimination* yields the same products as a Hofmann elimination (i.e., exhaustive methylation).

187

Notes for active learning

Notes for active learning

Notes for active learning

Alkynes – Detailed Explanations

1. E is correct.

In excess hydrogen gas, the triple bond of 3-heptyne is completely reduced to the alkane.

Platinum and palladium catalysts can be used to reduce alkynes to alkenes or alkanes.

2. C is correct.

Protonation of alkynes with acids generates the more substituted carbocation because this cation is the more stable intermediate. Because the cation exists on a vinyl carbon atom, this cation is a *vinyl cation*.

3. C is correct.

Use the following formulae to calculate the *degrees of unsaturation*:

C_nH_{2n+2}: for an alkane (0 degrees of unsaturation)

C_nH_{2n}: for an alkene or a ring (1 degree of unsaturation)

C_nH_{2n-2}: for an alkyne, 2 double bonds, 2 rings or 1 ring and 1 double bond (2 degrees of unsaturation).

The *general chemical formula for alkynes* is C_nH_{2n-2} because each *pi* bond of the alkyne represents one degree of unsaturation.

Cyclic alkynes have an additional degree of unsaturation because of the cyclic structure.

Therefore, C_9H_{16} is the molecular formula that describes an acyclic alkyne.

4. A is correct.

One *sigma* bond and two *pi* bonds are used to make the triple bond of alkynes.

Nitriles are another functional group that contains a triple bond.

5. A is correct.

Using a subscript of n for the number of carbons, the *degree of unsaturation* is:

Alkane: C_nH_{2n+2} = 0 degrees of unsaturation

Alkene: C_nH_{2n} = 1 degree of unsaturation (1 ring or 1 double bond)

Alkyne: C_nH_{2n-2} = 2 degrees of unsaturation (2 double bonds, 1 double bond and 1 ring or 2 rings)

6. D is correct.

Platinum and palladium are used to hydrogenate alkynes to alkenes (or alkanes) or reduce alkenes to alkanes.

$$H-C\equiv C-H \xrightarrow[\text{Pt}]{\text{1 eq. } H_2} \begin{array}{c} H \\ \diagdown \\ \diagup \\ H \end{array} C = C \begin{array}{c} H \\ \diagup \\ \diagdown \\ H \end{array} \xrightarrow[\text{Pt}]{\text{1 eq. } H_2} H-\overset{\overset{\displaystyle H}{|}}{\underset{\underset{\displaystyle H}{|}}{C}}-\overset{\overset{\displaystyle H}{|}}{\underset{\underset{\displaystyle H}{|}}{C}}-H$$

Two moles of hydrogen gas reduce the two pi bonds of the alkyne to an alkane.

7. B is correct.

Alkynes are triple bonded molecules made of hydrogen and carbon atoms.

The electronegativity difference between carbon and hydrogen is low, resulting in the molecule being less polar.

Molecules with little polarization may be more soluble in organic solvents as opposed to water.

8. A is correct.

Whenever a hydrocarbon is burned (adding O_2), the major byproducts of the reaction are water and carbon dioxide. Ash may form from the reaction, composed of carbon material that cannot undergo further oxidation.

9. C is correct.

$$H_3C-\!\!\!\equiv\!\!CH$$

Alkyne: C_nH_{2n-2} = 2 degrees of unsaturation due to the triple bond.

In the name of this molecule, the prefix is *pro–*, which indicates that the molecule is composed of three carbon atoms.

The *–yne* suffix indicates that a carbon-carbon triple bond exists in the molecule.

Therefore, propyne has three carbon atoms and four hydrogen atoms.

10. C is correct.

1-butyne is a gas at room temperature, and 1-propyne has an even lower boiling point, so it is a gas.

11. C is correct.

Two *pi* bonds use one mole of H_2 each, so 2 moles of hydrogen are consumed in the conversion.

12. D is correct.

Bromine atoms are added to both sides of the triple bond to produce a vicinal dibrominated alkene.

The addition product has the bromine atoms on opposite sides of the double bond; therefore, this addition proceeds through an *anti*-addition mechanism.

13. B is correct.

The substrate contains a carbon-carbon triple bond at the end of the chain. Therefore, to synthesize 2-hexanone from 1-hexyne, oxygen is introduced to the internal carbon atom of the alkene. This reaction requires aqueous acidic conditions so that addition proceeds as a Markovnikov addition.

The protonation of the alkyne results in the formation of a secondary vinyl cation.

This cation is trapped by water to produce an enol that tautomerizes to form the ketone product.

14. A is correct.

Radical hydrogenation of a C≡C triple bond in the presence of sodium metal and liquid ammonia adds two hydrogen atoms (i.e., reduction) across the double bond with *anti*-stereoselectivity, producing an *E* alkene.

The mechanism for reducing an alkyne to a trans (E) alkene

Lindlar reagent (i.e., H_2, Pd, $CaCo_3$, quinolone, and hexane) reduces the alkyne to the *cis* (*Z*) alkene.

Reaction for reducing an alkyne to a cis (Z) alkene

The Lindlar reagent, unlike the reagents of Na and NH_3, can be used to reduce a terminal alkyne to an alkene. Na and NH_3 is a "poison catalyst" and are unreactive with a terminal alkyne.

15. C is correct.

When terminal alkynes are treated with Lewis acids, such as mercury salts in aqueous conditions, the ketone forms the major product instead of the aldehyde.

The mercury cation is electron-deficient and forms a complex with the alkyne. This coordination increases the electrophilicity of the carbon atoms of the alkyne, and water adds to the internal carbon atom because the partial positive charge is larger at this position. This addition forms an enol (i.e., hydroxyl attached to a carbon in a double bond) that tautomerizes to the ketone.

A reduction step with sodium borohydride ($NaBH_4$) is not necessary because the carbon-mercury bond could break (to give Hg^{2+} and the enolate) when the ketone forms.

16. B is correct.

Although hydroxide and high temperatures are employed in this reaction, the potassium hydroxide base is not strong enough to catalyze the isomerization of the triple bond, which is why the internal, not terminal, alkyne is recovered from the reaction.

17. D is correct.

The oxymercuration-demercuration [$Hg(OAc)_2$] of alkynes occurs with Markovnikov addition to generate a ketone enol. This enol tautomerizes to form a ketone. Sodium borohydride ($NaBH_4$) then reduces the ketone to the secondary alcohol.

18. B is correct.

Hydrogenation (i.e., reduction) involves the addition of hydrogens (H_2) to an unsaturated molecule.

Catalytic hydrogenation (H_2/Pd or Pt) of an alkyne is susceptible to a further reduction to yield an alkane.

Alkynes can be reduced to stereospecific products with special reagents.

An alkyne yields a *cis* alkene which requires the Lindlar catalyst (i.e., H_2, Pd, $CaCo_3$, quinolone, and hexane) and a *trans* alkene with Ni (or Li) metal over NH_3 (*l*).

A: *oxidation* is an increase in the number of bonds to oxygen. Increasing the number of bonds to oxygen often results from decreasing the number of bonds to hydrogens.

C: adding H_2 (i.e., hydrogenation) is an addition, not a substitution, reaction.

D: *hydration* reactions add water to an unsaturated (i.e., alkene or alkyne) molecule.

E: *elimination* reaction increases the degree of unsaturation in a molecule. Elimination describes the conversion of an alkane to an alkene (or alkyne) or converting an alkene to an alkyne.

19. C is correct.

Using a subscript of n for the number of carbons, the *degrees of unsaturation* uses the following formulae:

Alkane: C_nH_{2n+2} = 0 degrees of unsaturation

Alkene: C_nH_{2n} = 1 degree of unsaturation

Alkyne: C_nH_{2n-2} = 2 degrees of unsaturation

The formula C_nH_{2n-2} is the general formula for acyclic alkynes.

The general molecular formula for cyclic alkynes is C_nH_{2n-4}.

Cyclic alkynes (i.e., bond angle of 180°) are typically larger-sized rings with at least 8 carbon atoms in the ring.

20. C is correct.

The higher the pK_a of a compound, the less acidic the molecule is and the stronger the *conjugate base* is.

The pK_a of water is $\approx$ 15-16.

The pK_a of the terminal alkynes is $\approx$ 25.

The pK_a of the N-H bonds of neutral amines is $\approx$ 36-38.

Therefore, water and the terminal alkyne (but-1-yne or butyne) are more acidic.

21. B is correct.

When an alkyne is reduced by sodium in liquid ammonia, a single electron is transferred to the alkyne to produce an anion. The intermediate is a vinyl anion because it is on the atom that is in the double bond.

The anion protonates to give the vinyl radical.

The only cations produced during the reaction are the Na^+.

22. C is correct.

Use the following formulae to calculate the degrees of unsaturation:

C_nH_{2n+2}: for an alkane (0 degrees of unsaturation)

C_nH_{2n}: for an alkene or a ring (1 degree of unsaturation)

C_nH_{2n-2}: for an alkyne, 2 double bonds, 2 rings or 1 ring and 1 double bond (2 degrees of unsaturation)

Molecular formula $C_{10}H_{16}$ (C_nH_{2n-6}) has 3 degrees of unsaturation. It is consistent with an acyclic molecule that contains two alkyne functional groups or three alkenes or two alkenes and one ring, etc.

A molecule with two triple bonds has 4 degrees of unsaturation (C_nH_{2n-8}) or $C_{10}H_{14}$.

23. D is correct.

A catalytic system, which may produce alkenes from alkynes, is the Lindlar catalyst (i.e., H_2, Pd, $CaCo_3$, quinolone, and hexane).

An alkyne yields a *cis* alkene when subjected to the Lindlar catalyst.

Hydrogenation reactions catalyzed by platinum or palladium result in the formation of alkane products.

24. C is correct.

The acetylide anion has a $pK_a \approx$ 28. Due to the large differences in electronegativity between oxygen and carbon atoms, ions that possess negatively charged oxygen atoms are relatively more stable than carbon anions.

The sodium methoxide is the most stable conjugate base, and therefore the least basic.

The CH_3Li is the Gilman reagent, and CH_3MgBr is the Grignard; both are strong bases with a pK_a greater than 40.

25. D is correct.

The hydration of the terminal alkyne with BH$_3$ proceeds with *anti*-Markovnikov regioselectivity.

Enol is on the left and the keto on the right

The enol intermediate tautomerizes to the keto product, whereby the keto product (more stable) is over 99% of the observed product.

26. B is correct.

1-butyne is a terminal alkyne.

Terminal alkynes have additional chemical properties, such as their ability to form anions when exposed to strong bases (e.g., the acetylide anion that forms with NaNH$_2$).

27. D is correct.

The bond order for an alkyne is larger than for an alkene.

The larger the bond order, the shorter the bond. Therefore, the *pi* bond in an alkyne is shorter.

Furthermore, there is less *p* orbital overlap present in an alkyne than in an alkene.

Because the internuclear overlap is lower, the *pi* bond is weaker.

28. A is correct.

The Grignard reagent (CH$_3$CH$_2$MgBr), as a carbanion, is a strong base.

In the terminal alkyne shown, an acid-base reaction occurs by deprotonating the alkyne and producing ethane.

29. C is correct.

The hydration of the terminal alkyne proceeds with Markovnikov regioselectivity to produce a ketone.

A: the enol intermediate tautomerizes to the keto product.

B: CH$_3$CH$_2$CH$_2$CH=CHOH is the enol intermediate of the *anti*-Markovnikov reaction (hydroboration with BH$_3$).

D: CH$_3$CH$_2$CH$_2$CH$_2$CHO is the aldehyde product of the *anti*-Markovnikov reaction (hydroboration with BH$_3$).

E: CH$_3$CH$_2$CH$_2$CH(OH)CH$_2$OH is the germinal diol as would be formed from the treatment of an alkene with OsO$_4$ (osmium tetroxide to form the *syn*-diol).

30. B is correct.

Alkynes can undergo bromination to yield compounds with four bromine atoms incorporated in their structures.

The first halogenation is expected to proceed more quickly than the second halogenation.

Bromine atoms are quite large (about the size of a tertbutyl group), and the first bromination increases the steric bulk of the reactant to form the intermediate alkene.

Furthermore, the bromine atoms are more electronegative than carbon, so the *pi* bond of the alkene intermediate is less electron-rich and less nucleophilic than the alkyne *pi* bond.

31. D is correct.

Alkynes are oxidized by two mechanisms to yield the Markovnikov or *anti*-Markovnikov product.

One of the *pi* bonds of the alkyne undergoes addition to yield an enol intermediate. The enol tautomerizes to generate the Markovnikov ketone or the *anti*-Markovnikov aldehyde.

32. A is correct.

The hydration of the alkyne forms a carbocation and proceeds through a Markovnikov-type mechanism.

The enol intermediate converts (i.e., tautomerizes) to the keto of the methyl phenyl ketone product.

33. C is correct.

The compound has five carbons, seven hydrogens, and one nitrogen.

Use the following formulae to calculate the *degrees of unsaturation*:

C_nH_{2n+2}: for an alkane (0 degrees of unsaturation)

C_nH_{2n}: for an alkene or a ring (1 degree of unsaturation)

C_nH_{2n-2}: for an alkyne, 2 double bonds, 2 rings or 1 ring and 1 double bond (2 degrees of unsaturation)

The molecule has 3 degrees of unsaturation.

Because one of the unsaturation elements is a ring, the molecule contains two *pi* bonds.

34. C is correct.

Alkynes can be oxidized to aldehydes or ketones as follows:

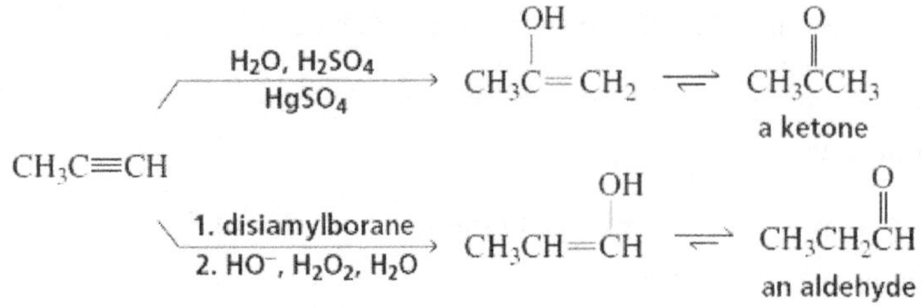

Disiamylborane (BH_3) is used for the hydroboration of alkynes (and alkenes) and involves peroxides in step 2.

The hydration of the alkyne (or alkene) proceeds through an *anti*-Markovnikov addition; the preference for the *anti*-Markovnikov addition is due to the minimization of steric interactions.

The peroxide (H_2O_2) and ⁻OH converts the RBH_2 bond to an enol (C=C–OH) of the *anti*-Markovnikov product.

The *enol* (alkene and alcohol attached to the same carbon atom) is less stable and tautomerizes (i.e., migration of a proton) to the aldehyde (aldehyde or ketone are referred to as keto) and not the final product of the reaction.

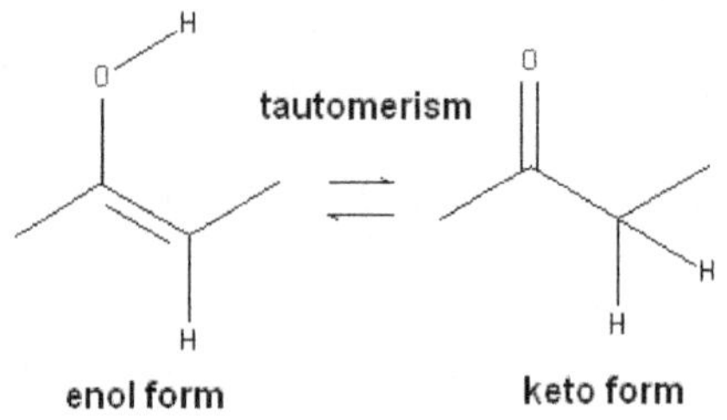

enol form   keto form

The keto and enol form are structural isomers, with the keto form more than 99% of the final yield due to stability.

35. C is correct.

Like alkenes, alkynes are electron-rich functional groups and function as nucleophiles that donate electron density to electron-seeking electrophiles. The reactivity of alkenes and alkynes is similar, and they interact with electrophiles in analogous ways.

36. B is correct.

In this reaction, the bromine adds to the alkene group of C_2H_4 and forms 1,2–dibromoethane. The reaction proceeds *via anti*-addition from the 3-membered bridge structure of the bromonium (i.e., halonium) ion.

A: hydrogen gas cannot be generated as a product from this reaction.

Carbon-carbon multibonds do not form from the given reaction conditions because the reagents do not include a base to eliminate the bromine(s) to form an alkene or alkyne.

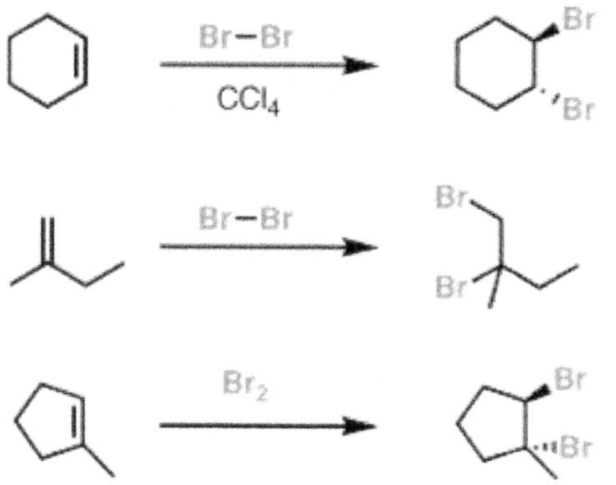

Sample *anti*-stereochemical products from the addition of bromine to an alkene. Each product has an enantiomer that is not shown.

Bromonium ion as an intermediate: bromonium ion

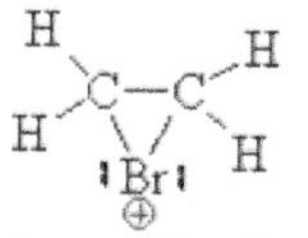

The reaction is regioselective (i.e., where) for the addition of the second nucleophile (i.e., Br^-) to the halonium (i.e., bromonium) structure. The incoming nucleophile attacks the more substituted atom.

Mechanism of Br_2 addition to an alkene:

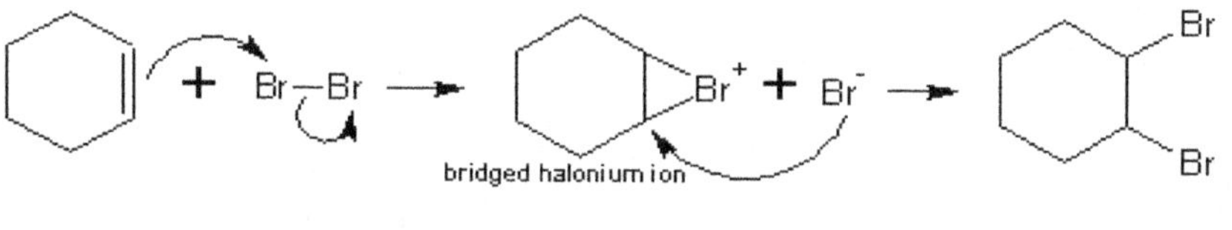

The incoming nucleophile attacks the bromonium bridged-structure ion at the most substituted position.

The bromonium ion (i.e., 3-membered bridged structure) undergoes S_N2 attack for *anti*-addition product formation. The stereochemical (i.e., *trans*) notation would include wedges and dashes.

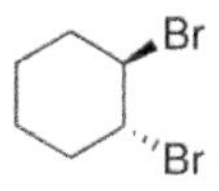

trans-1,2 dibromocyclohexane

Notes for active learning

Notes for active learning

Notes for active learning

Aromatic Compounds – Detailed Explanations

1. C is correct.

FeBr$_3$ acts as a catalyst to activate the alkyl bromide for electrophilic aromatic substitution (EAS) in this Friedel-Crafts alkylation. Since the ethyl substituent on ethylbenzene is slightly electron-donating, it functions as an *ortho*, *para* director for the substitution reaction.

Due to steric hindrance at the *ortho* position, *para* substitution is the major product.

2. B is correct.

The aromatic stabilization energy of benzene decreases the reactivity of its *pi* system relative to isolated or conjugated/nonaromatic alkenes. Because of this stabilization, arenes resist metal-catalyzed hydrogenation reactions and may require more specialized catalysts to facilitate their reductions.

3. E is correct.

Degenerate orbitals are with the same energy.

Bonding orbitals are below the horizontal plane, while the antibonding orbital is above.

In the molecular orbital (MO) diagram for benzene: MOs π2 and π3 are positioned in the second energy level, and π4 and π5 MOs are positioned on the third energy level.

Therefore, there are two pairs of degenerate MOs.

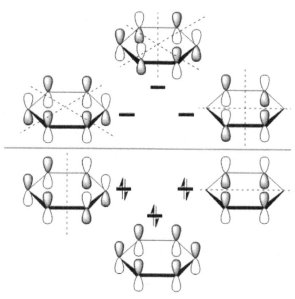

4. D is correct.

Because the nitrogen lone pair of the aniline is protonated, the group cannot donate electron density through the *pi* system of the aromatic ring.

Furthermore, the nitrogen atom has a formal charge of +1, and this group can function as a deactivating group because of its inductive effect.

5. A is correct.

Methyl substituents on benzene (toluene) are an ortho- / para-director and an activator (the electrophilic aromatic substitution rate is faster than benzene).

Friedel-Crafts alkylation reactions work best with electron-rich arenes.

Friedel-Crafts alkylation of toluene

---

6. D is correct.

I: The *ester* is the least activating moiety shown because the electron-withdrawing inductive effect of the electronegative oxygen on the carbonyl (ester group) reduces the electron density in the ring (i.e., deactivation).

II: *Methyl group* attached to the ring donates electron density *via* hyperconjugation and activates the ring slightly.

III: The lone pair of electrons on the ether resonates into the ring, which increases the electron density for EAS (i.e., activation).

7. C is correct.

Compared to benzene, electron-donating groups (such as ~OH) activate the ring towards EAS reactions.

Electron-withdrawing groups (such as the acetyl group) deactivate the ring, slowing EAS reactions.

Benzene undergoes bromination; however, its rate of bromination is less than for the phenol bromination.

8. D is correct.

The *pi* molecular orbitals of benzene are made from the overlap of six *p* orbitals. Because the number of molecular orbitals equals the number of atomic orbitals involved in the overlap, there are six molecular orbitals.

9. A is correct.

Four requirements for aromaticity:

       1) molecule is cyclic

       2) molecular is planar (flat)

       3) each atom is sp^2 hybridized (i.e., conjugated)

       4) the number of *pi* electrons satisfies Hückel's rule ($4n + 2$ *pi* electrons)

Aromatic rings can be positively or negatively charged if the 4 criteria are satisfied.

B, C, and D are antiaromatic with $4n$ *pi* electrons.

10. D is correct.

Phenol (i.e., hydroxybenzene) has an OH group on the benzene ring. The hydroxyl oxygen has two nonbonded pairs of electrons, which can be donated (*via* resonance) to the aromatic ring after the addition of an electrophile.

Electron-donating groups stabilize the cations formed upon adding a substituent to the *ortho* and *para* positions and therefore are *ortho/para*-directing activators.

The ~OH group is not notably bulky; there is little steric hindrance reducing substitution at the *ortho* position.

11. C is correct.

C: contains 4 π electrons and does *not* satisfy Hückel's rule for aromaticity ($4n + 2$ π electrons).

Additionally, the silicon atom is sp^3 hybridized and would not participate in aromatic conjugation.

12. A is correct.

Four requirements for aromaticity:

       1) molecule is cyclic

       2) molecular is planar (flat)

       3) each atom is sp^2 hybridized (i.e., conjugated)

       4) the number of *pi* electrons satisfies Hückel's rule ($4n + 2$ *pi* electrons)

Aromatic rings can be positively or negatively charged if the four criteria are satisfied.

Aromatic compounds have no saturated carbon atoms present in the aromatic ring.

The hybridization state of aromatic carbon atoms is sp^2, and the number of electrons in the aromatic system is consistent with Hückel's rule ($4n + 2$ π electrons).

13. D is correct.

The methyl group is an electron-donating substituent and therefore is an *ortho* / *para* director.

Due to steric hindrance at the *ortho* position, the *para* product is the major product.

14. C is correct.

The unknown cyclic hydrocarbon does not react with bromine in dichloromethane, carbon tetrachloride, or water. This means it cannot contain non-conjugated double or triple bonds; otherwise, the bromine would have added across the double bonds.

Since the unknown compound reacts when FeBr$_3$ is added, it must be benzene. The FeBr$_3$ acts as a *Lewis acid* and catalyzes aromatic electrophilic addition reactions.

Bromine is not a strong enough electrophile to disrupt the conjugated double bonding in the benzene ring.

However, adding the iron (III) bromide catalyst converts the bromine into a strong enough electrophile to add to the benzene ring.

15. D is correct.

The activating, deactivating, and directing (*ortho-* / *para-* and *meta*-directing) properties of aromatic substituents in electrophilic aromatic substitutions (EAS) and nucleophilic aromatic substitutions (NAS) are based on resonance stabilization or destabilization.

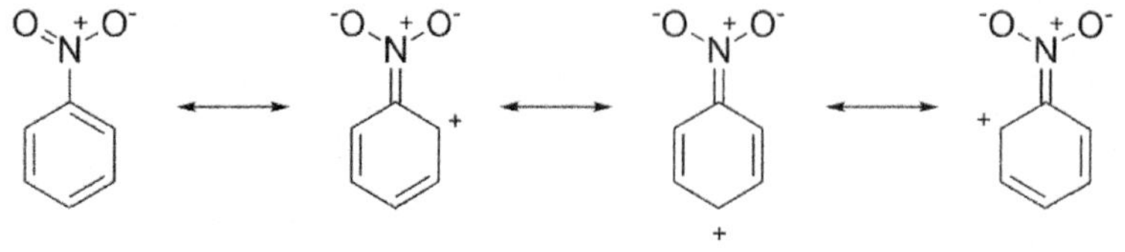

Resonance forms of nitrobenzene during EAS. Through resonance, electron-withdrawing groups introduce a partial positive charge at *ortho* and *para*. The *pi* bonds undergo delocalization for two hybrid structures:

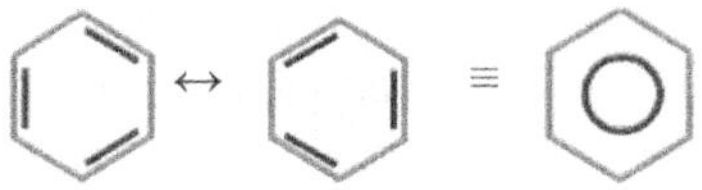

In EAS, the aromatic ring acts as a nucleophile, and the partially positive sites are less nucleophilic, making the electron-withdrawing group *meta*-directing.

In NAS, the aromatic ring acts as an electrophile, and the partially positive sites are more electrophilic, making the electron-withdrawing group an *ortho-* / *para*-director.

16. E is correct.

The two arenes activated by nitrogen heteroatoms are more nucleophilic.

The amide does not donate as strongly as the amine, so ring 1 is less nucleophilic than ring 3.

Ring 2 is only activated by the alkyl group and is the least reactive of the three.

17. A is correct.

The reaction is a Friedel-Crafts acylation using acetic anhydride $(CH_3CO)_2O$ as an acylating agent. The product is methyl ketone.

All halogens are deactivators but direct *ortho* / *para* because the halogen (like *ortho* / *para* directors) has lone pairs of electrons (on the atom attached to the ring). The lone pair helps stabilize the positive charge on the ring present in the resonance hybrid intermediates.

In general, deactivators (except for the halogens) are *meta* directors.

18. D is correct.

In EAS, the aromatic ring acts as a nucleophile attacking an electrophile.

Due to its aromaticity, however, the aromatic ring is relatively unreactive and is a poor nucleophile.

Extremely reactive electrophiles (and the addition of a Lewis base) are used to overcome this limitation.

19. C is correct.

Halides are electron-withdrawing (i.e., deactivating) and are *ortho/para*-directing.

Halogens are the exception to the general rule, which states that electron-withdrawing species are deactivating and *meta*-directing.

The halogens (despite being electron-withdrawing due to their high electronegativity) are *ortho/para*-directing with lone pairs of electrons localized, *via* resonance, to the electron density at *o/p* positions.

Resonance hybrids show the anion at both ortho positions

Note that the resonance structures include an anion at the *para* position.

Therefore, like atoms with lone pairs of electrons attached to the ring, halogens are *ortho-para* directors.

The resonance structure forms a double bond between the halide bearing a formal positive charge and the phenyl ring; therefore, it is not a significant resonance structure and cannot overcome the deactivating (due to electronegativity) effect caused by induction (along the *sigma* bond).

20. E is correct.

When 1,3-cyclopentadiene reacts with sodium metal, it is converted from nonaromatic to aromatic.

According to Hückel's rule, a planar cyclic compound is aromatic if conjugated (adjacent sp^2 hybridized carbon atoms) and has 4n + 2 *pi* electrons (where n is any whole number).

21. B is correct.

Carbonyl compounds are *meta*-directing in EAS reactions.

Since the nitro and carbonyl groups are deactivating, disubstitution is slow, and single *meta* substitution predominates.

22. D is correct.

Halogens are electron-withdrawing and deactivate a benzene ring toward electrophilic aromatic substitution, so bromobenzene undergoes nitration slower than benzene.

23. C is correct.

In electrophilic aromatic substitution, the aromatic ring acts as a nucleophile, attacking an electrophile that has been treated with a Lewis acid (e.g., $FeBr_3$, $AlCL_3$).

Deprotonation of the aromatic ring at the site of the attack reforms the double bond (an elimination reaction) and restores aromaticity.

The overall reaction substitutes an electrophile (e.g., Br, CH_3, RCO, HSO_3) for hydrogen on the aromatic ring.

24. D is correct.

The halogens are deactivating due to their high electronegativity. However, like *ortho / para*-directors, the halogens have a lone pair of electrons on the atom attached to the ring.

Alkyl chains do not have lone pairs of electrons on the C attached to the ring but are *ortho / para* directors due to hyperconjugation.

25. C is correct.

The reactivity of aromatic molecules toward *electrophilic aromatic substitution* (EAS) depends on the substituents on benzene.

Electron-donating substituents increase the electron density of the benzene ring and therefore activate benzene towards EAS.

Electron-withdrawing substituents deactivate the ring, making it less susceptible to EAS. The benzene ring is deactivated by the electron-withdrawing effects of the Cl and NH_3^+ substituents, and the ring is deactivated (compared to benzene) to EAS.

A: p-H_3CCH_2O–C_6H_4–O–CH_2CH_3 has two electron-donating ethoxy substituents and is highly reactive to EAS.

B: p-O_2N–C_6H_4–NH–CH_3 contains strong electron-withdrawing effects from the nitro (NO_2). The N of the NO_2 group has a formal charge of +, while the single-bonded O has a formal charge of –.

The NO_2 group offsets the strong electron-donating amino group (lone pair of electrons on N), so the molecule is only slightly reactive to EAS.

D: p-CH_3CH_2–C_6H_4–CH_2CH_3 contains two electron-donating (i.e., activating) ethyl substituents and is more reactive towards EAS.

E: benzene is the reference molecule to determine if substituents are activating (relative to benzene) or deactivating (relative to benzene).

26. C is correct.

The carbon atoms of benzene are sp^2 hybridized.

Non-planar molecules cannot be aromatic because the *pi* system must be planar (i.e., flat).

A *Kekule structure* is a Lewis structure with covalently bonded electron pairs drawn as lines. The Kekule structures illustrate the two most significant resonance contributors of benzene.

The alternating single and double drawn for benzene exist as a hybrid resonance structure from the delocalization.

Benzene with alternating double and single bonds – hybrid structure as bottom structure.

27. A is correct.

Addition reactions are typically not observed for aromatic compounds because the aromaticity is restored during their substitution reactions. When aromatic functional groups react, they may temporarily lose their aromaticity (i.e., high-energy resonance hybrids are the intermediates), and its restoration greatly increases the stability of the molecule.

Electrophilic aromatic substitution (EAS) reactions are favored over nucleophilic aromatic addition (NAS) reactions for aromatic compounds.

28. D is correct.

The double bonds in benzene are less reactive than in a non-aromatic alkene because addition (e.g., hydrogenation) disrupts the aromaticity (i.e., delocalization) of the ring, making it less stable.

Applying heat and high pressure with the Rh catalyst permits benzene to overcome the energy of activation necessary to transform the highly stable benzene molecule into a non-aromatic product.

29. D is correct.

$CH_3C_6H_5 + H_2$, Rh / C is a reduction reaction with a powerful reducing agent capable of disrupting the stability of the aromatic ring.

The regents reduce the benzene ring catalytically *via* hydrogenation to form cyclohexane.

Therefore, this is not an electrophilic aromatic substitution.

In general, an aromatic ring is especially susceptible to electrophilic aromatic substitution (EAS) with the Lewis acid (e.g., $FeBr_3$, $AlCl_3$ or H_2SO_4).

A: $CH_3C_6H_5 + C_6H_5CH_2CH_2Cl$ / $AlCl_3$ is an example of Friedel-Crafts alkylation (EAS), whereby toluene (benzene with a methyl substituent) reacts with an alkyl chloride with the Lewis acid aluminum trichloride ($AlCl_3$).

The Lewis acid removes chloride from the alkyl halide, forming a carbocation which is then attacked by the benzene ring.

B: $CH_3C_6H_5 + Br_2$ / $FeBr_3$ is an example of electrophilic aromatic substitution (EAS). $FeBr_3$ (similar to $AlCl_3$) is a Lewis acid.

Toluene is activating, and the Br substitutes in the *ortho / para* position.

C: $CH_3C_6H_5 + CH_3CH_2CH_2COCl$ / $AlCl_3$ is an example of Friedel-Crafts acylation (EAS), whereby toluene reacts with an acyl chloride in the presence of the Lewis acid aluminum trichloride ($AlCl_3$).

The Lewis acid removes chloride from the acyl halide, forming a carbocation which is then attacked by the benzene ring. Then a proton is removed to restore the aromaticity of the original ring structure.

E: $C_6H_6 + HSO_3$ / H_2SO_4 is an example of the EAS reaction for sulfonation of a benzene ring.

30. D is correct.

A: of the two substituents, the chloro group is *para*-directing, so it should be substituted first.

Additionally, Na / NH₃ results in the single *trans* hydrogenation of alkenes but does not substitute a nitro group in an EAS reaction.

B: of the two substituents, the chloro group is *para*-directing, so it should be substituted first.

C: while HCl / H₂O adds H and Cl across the double bonds of alkenes, these conditions do not substitute Cl in EAS reactions.

E: Cl₂ / CCl₄ are the conditions to dechlorinate an alkene.

Benzene does not undergo addition reactions due to aromaticity.

31. A is correct.

Benzene is aromatic and undergoes electrophilic aromatic substitution (EAS) with the addition of a Lewis acid (e.g., AlCl₃, FeBr₃ or H₂SO₄).

The reagents of SO₃ and concentrated H₂SO₄ are used to sulfonate aromatic compounds, whereby a SO₃H group is substituted onto the benzene ring.

Halogens are *ortho* and *para* directing deactivators.

Therefore, the product is a mixture of *ortho*- and *para*-bromobenzenesulfonic acid.

B: the bromine is not displaced from the aromatic benzene ring and replaced with hydrogen to form benzene.

C: the SO₃H group does not substitute for the bromine of bromobenzene.

D: *meta*- is not formed because halogens are *ortho* and *para* directing deactivators.

E: toluene is benzene with a methyl group attached.

32. A is correct.

Substituents on an aromatic ring affect the rate at which electrophilic aromatic substitution reactions occur.

Since the ring acts as a nucleophile in these reactions, electron-donating substituents increase the rate of reaction, while electron-withdrawing substituents decrease the rate of reaction.

The bromine substituent (III) is slightly deactivating (due to its electronegativity), making it less reactive than benzene (I).

The nitro group is extremely deactivating (due to resonance), making nitrobenzene (II) less reactive than bromobenzene (III).

33. B is correct.

Benzene is a cyclic aromatic hydrocarbon that has 4 degrees of unsaturation.

The *pi* bonds in the molecule are delocalized and impart aromaticity to the molecule.

34. C is correct.

Each molecule has nitro ($\sim NO_2$) and hydroxyl ($\sim OH$) functional groups to hydrogen-bond.

Proximity is needed for either intramolecular (within the molecule) or intermolecular (between molecules) bonding.

The alignment of the functional groups permitting hydrogen bonding depends on the shape of the molecule.

The melting points (transition from packed molecules in a solid to liquid phase), boiling points (transition from associated molecules in a liquid to independent molecules in the gas phase), and water solubility of polar molecules are related to the presence and quantity of intermolecular hydrogen bonding.

The *meta-* and *para-*nitrophenol are more water-soluble and have higher melting points than *ortho-*nitrophenol because *ortho-*nitrophenol tends to form intramolecular hydrogen bonds instead of intermolecular hydrogen bonds.

Intramolecular hydrogen bonds for *ortho-*nitrophenol make the molecule independent so that it takes less energy to disrupt the lattice structure of the molecules (melting).

Likewise, intramolecular hydrogen bonding reduces the molecule's ability to form hydrogen bonds with water, and therefore the molecule is less water-soluble.

A: *meta-* and *para-*nitrophenol form strong intermolecular hydrogen bonds, leading to a higher melting point.

The nitro and hydroxyl groups form hydrogen bonds with water, and the molecules are more water-soluble.

B: *ortho-*nitrophenol forms some intermolecular hydrogen bonds, but less than *meta-* and *para-* nitrophenol.

*Meta-*nitrophenol forms weak intramolecular bonds due to the large distance between the functional groups.

D: *para-*nitrophenol has the nitro and hydroxyl substituents at opposite ends of the flat molecule and cannot form intramolecular hydrogen bonds.

35. A is correct.

Hückel's rule predicts that for a monocyclic compound to be aromatic, there must be a fully conjugated *pi* (sp^2 hybridization at each atom in the ring) containing ($4n + 2$) *pi* electrons.

Two *pi* electrons are contributed by each of the double bonds.

The lone pair of electrons on a double-bonded N is perpendicular to the *pi* cloud and does not count as the number of *pi* electrons for Hückel's rule.

Note: when N is in a single bond, the unshared electrons parallel the *pi* system count toward aromaticity.

Benzimidazoline is not fully conjugated because there is a $\sim CH_2\sim$ (sp^3) group in the ring.

Cyclic conjugation is necessary for a molecule to be aromatic.

B: thiophene has an sp^2 hybridized sulfur (like oxygen) and has a lone pair of electrons counted as in the ring. The number of *pi* electrons is 6.

continued…

C: quinoline has 10 *pi* electrons and therefore is aromatic.

The lone pair of electrons on a double-bonded N is perpendicular to the *pi* cloud and does not count as the number of *pi* electrons for Hückel's rule.

D: thiazole has 6 *pi* electrons and therefore is aromatic.

The lone pair of electrons on a double-bonded N is perpendicular to the *pi* cloud and does not count as *pi* electrons for Hückel's rule.

Sulfur (like oxygen) is sp^2 hybridized and has a lone pair of electrons counted as in the ring.

E: imidazole has 6 *pi* electrons and therefore is aromatic.

The lone pair of electrons on a double-bonded N is perpendicular to the *pi* cloud and does not count as *pi* electrons for Hückel's rule.

The lone pair of electrons on a single bonded N is part of the *pi* cloud and counts as *pi* electrons for Hückel's rule.

36. D is correct.

Degrees of unsaturation:

double bonds = 1 degree of unsaturation

triple bonds = 2 degrees of unsaturation

rings = 1 degree of unsaturation

Using the degree of unsaturation calculation:

benzene (1 ring and 3 double bonds) = 4 degrees of unsaturation

Notes for active learning

Notes for active learning

Alcohols – Detailed Explanations

1. B is correct.

Alcohols follow the same trend for boiling points as alkanes, with longer chain molecules having higher boiling points. Hexanol is the longest chain and therefore has the highest boiling point.

2. E is correct.

When phenols are deprotonated (i.e., acting as an acid), a phenoxide ion (i.e., phenolate ion) is produced, as shown. The pK_a of phenols is much lower than it is for alcohols.

Methanol has a pK_a of 16, while phenols have pK_a values ≈ 9.9.

3. C is correct.

The formation of an inorganic ester by adding alcohol and phosphoric acid is an example of dehydration synthesis because an equivalent of water is lost during the process.

4. E is correct.

No carbon-oxygen *pi* bonds exist in alcohols (hydroxyl) functional groups.

Carbonyl (C=O) groups (i.e., carbon double bonded to oxygen) indicate ketones, aldehydes, or carboxylic acid derivatives (acyl halide, anhydride, ester, and amide).

5. A is correct.

Draw the structure of known compounds or the product of the reaction.

Ethanoate is an ester that has an *n*-propoxy substituent. Therefore, the alcohol that should be used is 1-propanol, and the remaining component is ethanoic acid.

6. C is correct.

The five-carbon molecule of *n*-pentanol has the largest alkyl portion (i.e., the greatest number of London forces). It possesses hydroxyl, which allows it to hydrogen bond (increases boiling point).

An overall molecular dipole exists for this molecule that contributes to its high boiling point.

7. B is correct.

The ~OH (hydroxyl) group is characteristic of alcohol and carboxylic acids (includes a carbonyl group).

8. D is correct.

Sodium dichromate ($Na_2Cr_2O_7$) is a strong oxidizing agent which converts primary alcohols to carboxylic acids.

Sodium dichromate converts secondary alcohols to ketones.

9. B is correct.

Thionyl chloride (SOCl₂) is a reagent that converts primary and secondary alcohols to alkyl chlorides.

Phosphorous tribromide (PBr₃) is a reagent that converts primary and secondary alcohols to alkyl bromides.

10. A is correct.

The molecule has an alkene on the righ, alcohol near the lower right portion, and a fused ether functional group.

11. B is correct.

Molecules containing rings or multibonds are molecules with degrees of unsaturation.

A completely saturated compound only consists of single bonds (*sigma* bonds).

12. C is correct.

Primary alcohols have an ~OH group attached to a carbon that is connected to another carbon atom.

Secondary alcohols possess an ~OH group bonded to a carbon attached to two other carbon atoms.

Tertiary alcohols have ~OH groups bonded to carbon atoms attached to three other carbon atoms.

13. C is correct. Carboxylic acids (~COOH) contain an ~OH group bonded to carbonyls (C=O).

Oximes (C=N–OH) are functional groups containing an ~OH group; they are used for reductive amination.

14. B is correct

The reaction between (*S*)-2-heptanol and SOCl₂ (thionyl chloride) proceeds *via* an S$_N$2 reaction mechanism.

An addition-elimination sequence occurs at the S=O double bond, then substitution by Cl⁻ of the alcohol gives the inverted (*R*)-2-chloroheptane product.

15. A is correct.

The reaction of 1-pentanol + acetic acid

The alkoxy group has five carbon atoms, and an acyl portion is an acetyl group.

Acetyl group

Acetate is the root of this molecule.

16. B is correct.

Ethers follow the same trend as alkanes, so dihexyl ether has the highest boiling point because it has the greatest molecular weight and has the largest surface area.

17. E is correct.

The most notable intermolecular force for water is hydrogen bonding.

Alcohols donate and receive hydrogen bonds.

Thiols (S–H bonds) have much smaller dipoles than O–H, so they do not participate in hydrogen bonding.

18. B is correct.

The tosyl group adds with retention of stereochemistry because the C–O bond is not broken.

Tosylation of secondary alcohol makes it a better leaving group.

The chloride anion is a good nucleophile, displacing the tosylate to form the secondary alkyl chloride.

D: shows a product that has retained stereospecificity (no inversion).

This retention of stereochemistry occurs when an S_N2 reaction (i.e., inversion) is followed by a second S_N2.

19. D is correct.

For a given class of compounds, the lower the molecular weight, the lower the boiling point.

Alcohols follow the same trend for the boiling point as alkanes.

Ethanol is a two-carbon chain (i.e., lowest molecular weight) with hydrogen bonding (e.g., alcohols and carboxylic acids). It has the lowest molecular weight of the choices and therefore has the lowest boiling point.

20. D is correct.

HBr is a strong acid that protonates the oxygen atom of the alcohol. Then, either the bromide displaces the water to give 1-bromo-2-methylpropane, or a hydride shift occurs to form the tertiary carbocation, which can be trapped by the bromide resulting in 2-bromo-2-methylpropane.

21. D is correct.

The reaction between propanol and PBr₃ (phosphorous tribromide) proceeds *via* an S_N2 reaction mechanism.

An addition-elimination sequence occurs to the P–Br bond, then substitution by Br⁻ of the alcohol gives the inverted (*R/S*) product (i.e., bromopropane).

22. D is correct.

Primary alcohols are oxidized to carboxylic acids with an oxidizing agent (e.g., CrO_3 in HCl).

Oxidation:

        primary alcohol → aldehyde → carboxylic acid

        secondary alcohol → ketone

        tertiary alcohol → no reaction

23. D is correct.

The *boiling points* of compounds are determined by two general factors: molecular weight and intermolecular interactions.

The higher the *molecular weight*, the harder it is to "push" it into the gas phase; the higher the boiling point.

Similarly, the stronger the *intermolecular interactions*, the more energy is required to disrupt them and separate the molecules in the gas phase, hence the higher the boiling point.

Alcohols participate in hydrogen bonding due to the hydroxyl (~OH) group.

The alkane, alkene, ether, and alkyl halide only participate in dipole-dipole interactions and London forces.

24. C is correct.

2-hexanol is secondary alcohol and can be oxidized to a ketone with an oxidizing agent (e.g., CrO_3 in HCl).

The carbon atom of the alcohol is only bonded to one other hydrogen atom; therefore, the highest oxidation state it can acquire is the ketone oxidation state (i.e., +2).

Oxidation: primary alcohol → aldehyde → carboxylic acid

                  secondary alcohol → ketone

                  tertiary alcohol → no reaction

25. D is correct.

Alcohols of the same chain length as alkanes, alkenes, and alkynes have higher boiling points due to hydrogen bonding of the ~OH group.

Alkanes, alkenes, and alkynes are not able to form hydrogen bonds.

26. B is correct.

Carbonyl (C=O) groups indicate ketones, aldehydes, or carboxylic acid derivatives (acyl halides, anhydrides, esters, and amides).

Ethers are noted as R–O–R and do not contain carbonyl groups.

27. A is correct.

For alkenes, allylic refers to an atom attached to a carbon adjacent (β) to the double bond.

For carbonyl (C=O) compounds (aldehydes, ketones, acyl halides, anhydrides, carboxylic acids, esters, and amides), the position adjacent to the C of the C=O is the α position.

The hydroxyl (~OH) group of allylic alcohols is one carbon-carbon *sigma* bond away from the double bond.

Vinyl refers to an atom attached to carbon on a double bond.

28. A is correct.

The *electronegativity* of the oxygen atom in alcohol helps stabilize the negative charge of the conjugate base (i.e., negative oxygen) of the alcohol.

A more stable conjugate base results in a stronger acid (more readily dissociating its proton).

Secondary alcohols are more acidic than tertiary alcohols.

29. A is correct.

Pyridinium chlorochromate (PCC) is a gentle oxidizing agent which converts primary alcohols to aldehydes.

PCC is used to convert secondary alcohols to ketones.

B: carboxylic acids require a more powerful oxidizing agent (e.g., Jones reagent; CrO_3, H_2SO_4 and acetone)

C: alkenes proceed *via* E_1 when the alcohol is subjected to mineral acid (e.g., H_2SO_4)

D: terminal alkyl halides are produced in two steps.

First, alcohol becomes an alkene (E_1 when the alcohol is subjected to a mineral acid, H_2SO_4).

The alkene is halogenated in *anti*-Markovnikov regiochemistry when peroxides (H_2O_2) are in the reaction.

E: an alkyne requires an initial alkene, followed by Br_2 (or Cl_2) for the dibromo compound, followed by elimination with two equivalents of a base to yield the alkyne.

30. C is correct.

Tertiary alcohol undergoes E_1 reactions faster (i.e., due to the stability of the carbocation intermediate) than secondary alcohols, which can dehydrate at a faster rate than primary alcohols.

31. D is correct.

A *tosyl group* (Tos) is $CH_3C_6H_4SO_2$ (derived from $CH_3C_6H_4SO_2Cl$) and forms esters and amides of tosylic acid.

Tosylates are used to increase the efficiency of the original hydroxyl as a leaving group.

Unlike PBr_3 or $SOCl_2$ (both *via* S_N2), the reaction mechanism preserves the bond between the carbon and the O of the hydroxyl. Therefore, no inversion of stereochemistry occurs (first step in this example) using a tosylate.

The first step with the tosylate results in retention of the chiral center, and the second step (i.e., Cl^- as a nucleophile) produces an inverted product.

32. D is correct.

Aldehydes and ketones undergo tautomerization to exist in equilibrium between the keto and enol forms.

Most molecules (~99%) exist predominantly in the keto form because the carbon-oxygen (carbonyl) double bond is more stable than the hydroxyl on the double bond of the enol.

Keto   *Enol*

Phenols are a few aldehydes/ketones existing predominantly as enols form in keto-enol tautomer equilibrium.

The conjugated benzene ring system of phenol provides stability for the enol form.

The keto form of phenol lacks conjugation because the carbon in the ring is sp^3 hybridized.

When the phenol molecule assumes the keto form, aromaticity is lost, and the molecule becomes less stable.

Enol   *Keto*   Therefore, the keto form is non-aromatic and thus less stable.

Aromatic molecules are cyclic, planar, have conjugated double bonds (i.e., sp^2 at each atom), and satisfy Hückel's number of *pi* electrons (4n + 2, where n is an integer).

Anti-aromatic compounds are cyclic, planar, have conjugated double bonds, but have 4n (e.g., 4, 8, 12 and so on) *pi* electrons and therefore are unstable.

Nonaromatic compounds do not meet the four criteria needed for aromatic compounds: cyclic, planar, conjugated double bonds, and Hückel's number of *pi* electrons.

33. C is correct.

Treatment of *salicylic acid* (i.e., aspirin) with methanol (CH_3OH) and dry acid are conditions for synthesizing an ester in a mechanism is *Fischer esterification*:

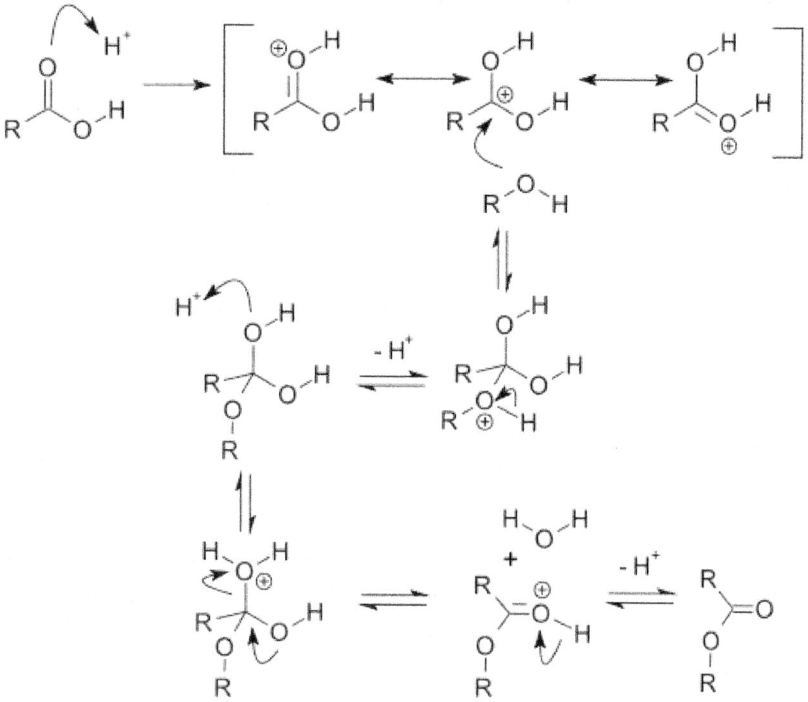

34. B is correct.

The reaction between (R)-2-hexanol and PBr_3 (phosphorous tribromide) proceeds *via* an S_N2 mechanism.

An addition-elimination sequence occurs in the P–Br bond, then substitution by Br^- of the alcohol gives the inverted (S)-2-bromohexane product.

35. B is correct.

Esterification occurs when a carboxylic acid reacts with alcohol under catalytic acidic conditions to form an ester + water.

A: C_6H_5OH and CH_3CH_2Br form an ether *via* Williamson (S_N2) ether synthesis when the alcohol reacts with the alkyl halide.

C: $CH_3COOH + SOCl_2$ is the S_N2 reaction of a carboxylic acid with thionyl chloride, and an acyl halide is formed.

D: $2CH_3OH + H_2SO_4$, form dimethyl ether from methanol and catalytic acid (e.g., sulfuric acid).

E: $CH_3CH_2Br + CH_3CH_2O^-Na^+$ forms an ether *via* Williamson (S_N2) ether synthesis when alcohol reacts with an alkyl halide.

The requirement is that the alkyl halide is less substituted because the reaction proceeds *via* S_N2.

36. B is correct.

The hydrobromic acid protonates the secondary alcohol that dissociates as water.

The secondary carbocation, formed as an intermediate, is repositioned to the tertiary position through an alkyl (i.e., methide) shift.

After the methide shift, this more stable tertiary carbocation is then attacked by the bromide ion.

Notes for active learning

Notes for active learning

Appendix

Glossary of Organic Chemistry Terms

A

Acetal – product formed by the reaction of an aldehyde with *alcohol*; the general structure of an acetal is:

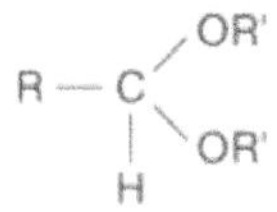

R — C (OR')(OR')(H)

Achiral (or non-chiral) – the opposite of *chiral*; can be superimposed on its mirror image (e.g., CH_4); do not rotate plane-polarized light.

Acid – an agent able to produce positively charged hydrogen ions (H^+); since the hydrogen ion is a bare proton, it usually exists in a solvated form (such as H_3O^+); a proton donor or an electron pair acceptor; see *Brønsted-Lowry theory of acids and bases*, *Lewis acid* and *Lewis base*.

Acid-base reaction – a neutralization reaction in which the products are salt and water.

Activated complex – molecules at an unstable intermediate stage in a reaction.

Activating group – a substituent that increases the rate of electrophilic aromatic substitution (EAS) when bonded to an aromatic ring.

Activation energy – the minimum energy which reacting species must possess in order to be able to form an "activated complex," or "transition state," before proceeding to the products; the difference in potential energy between the ground state and the transition state of molecules; molecules of reactants must have this amount of energy to proceed to the product state; the activation energy (E_a) may be derived from the temperature dependence of the reaction rate using the *Arrhenius equation*.

Acyl group – a substituent with the following structure, where R can be an alkyl or aryl group:

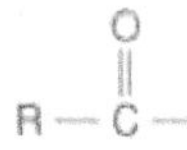

R — C(=O) —

Acyl halide – a compound with the general structural formula:

R — C(=O) — X

Acylation – a reaction in which an acyl group is added to a molecule.

Acylium ion – the resonance stabilized cation:

$$R\overset{+}{C} = \overset{..}{O}: \longleftrightarrow RC \equiv \overset{+}{O}:$$

Addition – a reaction that produces a new compound by combining the elements of the original reactants.

Addition elimination mechanism – the two-stage mechanism by which nucleophilic *aromatic* substitution (NAS) occurs; in the first stage, the addition of the nucleophile to the carbon bearing the *leaving group* occurs; an elimination follows in which the leaving group is expelled.

Addition reactions – an unsaturated system is saturated or partly saturated by adding a molecule across the multiple bonds (e.g., adding bromine to ethene to form 1,2-dibromoethane).

Adduct – the product of an addition reaction.

Alcohol – a molecule containing a hydroxyl (~OH) group; also, a functional group.

Aldehyde – a molecule containing a terminal carbonyl (~CHO) group; also, a functional group.

Alicyclic compound – an *aliphatic cyclic* hydrocarbon; a compound contains a ring but not an *aromatic* ring; see *aliphatic compound* and *cyclization*.

Aliphatic compound – a straight-chain or branched-chain hydrocarbon, an *alkane*, *alkene* or *alkyne*.

Alkaloid – organic substances occurring naturally, which are basic, forming salts with acids; the basic group is usually an amino function.

Alkane – a hydrocarbon that contains only single covalent bonds (i.e., containing only C–H and C–C single bonds); the general *alkane* formula is C_nH_{2n+2}.

Alkene – a molecule containing one or more carbon-carbon double bonds; also, a *functional group*.

Alkoxide ion – an anion formed by removing a proton from an *alcohol*; the RO^- ion.

Alkoxy free radical – formed by homolytic cleavage of an *alcohol* ~OH bond; the $RO\cdot$ radical.

Alkyl group – an *alkane* molecule from which a hydrogen atom has been removed; abbreviated as "R" in structural formulas.

Alkyl halide – a hydrocarbon that contains a halogen substituent, such as fluorine, chlorine, bromine, or iodine.

Alkyl-substituted cycloalkane – a cyclic hydrocarbon to which one or more *alkyl group*s are bonded; compare with *cycloalkyl alkane*.

Alkylation – a reaction in which an *alkyl group* is added to a molecule.

Alkyne – a molecule containing one or more carbon-carbon triple bonds; also, a functional group; the general formula is C_nH_{2n-2}.

Allyl group – the $H_2C=CHCH_2$ group contains 3 carbon atoms and a double bond, $C_1=C_2–C_3$, where C_3 is the "allylic position" or "*allylic carbon* atom."

Allylic carbon – a sp^3 carbon adjacent to a double bond.

Allylic carbocation – the $H_2C=CHCH_2^+$ ion.

Allylic rearrangement – the migration of a double bond in a 3-carbon system from carbon atoms one and two to carbon atoms two and three (e.g., $C_1=C_2–C_3–X$ to $X–C_1–C_2=C_3$).

Analogue – in organic chemistry, chemicals that are similar but not identical (e.g., the hydrocarbons are similar, but an *alkane* is different from *alkenes* and *alkynes* because of the types of bonds they contain; therefore, an *alkane* and an *alkene* are analogs).

Angle of rotation (α) – in a polarimeter, the angle right or left in which plane-polarized light is turned after passing through an optically active compound in solution.

Amide – a molecule containing a carbonyl group attached to nitrogen (~CONR$_2$); also, a functional group.

Amine – a molecule containing isolated nitrogen (NR$_3$); also, a functional group.

Anion – a negatively charged ion.

Anomers – the specific term used to describe carbohydrate stereoisomers differing only in configuration at the hemiacetal carbon atom.

***Anti*-addition** – a reaction in which the two groups of a reagent X–Y add on the opposite faces of a carbon-carbon bond.

***Anti*-aromatic** – a highly unstable planar ring system with 4*n pi* electrons.

Antibonding molecular orbital – contains more energy than the atomic orbitals (AO) from which it was formed; an electron is less stable in an antibonding orbital than in its original atomic orbital.

***Anti*-conformation** – a type of staggered conformation in which the two big groups are opposite each other in a *Newman projection*.

***Anti*-Markovnikov addition** – a reaction in which the hydrogen atom of a hydrogen halide bonds to the carbon of a double bond that is bonded to *fewer* hydrogen atoms; the addition takes place *via* a free-radical intermediate rather than a carbocation; compare with *Markovnikov rule*.

***Anti*-periplanar (anti-coplanar)** – the conformation in which hydrogen and the leaving group are in the same plane and on opposite sides of a carbon-carbon single bond; also, the conformation required for E$_2$ elimination.

Aprotic solvents – solvents that do not contain O–H or N–H bonds.

Arene – an *Aromatic* hydrocarbon.

Aromatic – possesses aromaticity; aromaticity is the property of planar (or nearly planar) cyclic, conjugated systems having (4n + 2) conjugated *pi* electrons; the delocalization of the (4n + 2) *pi* electrons give them exceptional stability (aromatic compounds are unusually stable compounds); for benzene, the most common aromatic system (n = 1, therefore 6 *pi* electrons), the aromaticity confers the characteristic reactivity of electrophilic substitution.

Aromatic compound – possesses a closed-shell electron configuration and resonance; obeys *Hückel's rule*.

Aryl – an *aromatic* group as a substituent.

Aryl group – a group, produced by the removal of a proton from an *aromatic* molecule.

Aryl halide – a compound in which a halogen atom is attached to an *aromatic* ring.

Association – a term applied to the combination of molecules of a substance with one another to form more complex systems; see *dissociation* and *dissociation constant*.

Asymmetry – a term applied to an object or molecule that does not possess symmetry.

Asymmetric induction – a term applied to the selective synthesis of one diastereomeric form of a compound resulting from the influence of an existing *chiral* center adjacent to the developing asymmetric carbon atom; this usually arises because, for steric reasons, the incoming atom or group does not have equal access to both sides of the molecule.

Atom – the smallest amount of an element; a nucleus surrounded by electrons.

Atomic mass (A) – the sum of the weights of the protons and neutrons in an atom; a proton and neutron each have a mass of 1 atomic mass unit.

Atomic number (Z) – the number of protons or electrons in an atom.

Atomic 1s orbital – the spherical orbital nearest the nucleus of an atom.

Atomic orbital – a region in space around the nucleus of an atom where the probability of finding an electron is high, which may be described in terms of the four quantum numbers.

Atomic p orbital – an hourglass-shaped orbital, oriented on x, y and z-axes in three-dimensional space.

Atomic s orbital – a spherical orbital.

Avogadro's constant – number of particles (atoms or molecules) in one mole of a pure substance: 6.022×10^{23}.

Axial bond – a bond perpendicular to the equator of the ring (up or down), typically in a chair cyclohexane.

B

Baeyer reagent – cold, dilute potassium permanganate; used to oxidize *alkenes* and *alkynes*.

Base – a substance that can combine with a proton (i.e., a proton acceptor or an electron-pair donor); see *Brønsted-Lowry theory of acids and bases*, *Lewis acid* and *Lewis base*.

Benzene (Benzenoid) ring – an *Aromatic* ring with a benzene-like structure.

Benzyl group – a *benzene ring* plus a methylene (~CH_2~) unit: $C_6H_5CH_2$.

Benzylic position – the position of carbon attached to a *benzene ring*.

Benzyne – an unstable intermediate consisting of a benzene ring with an additional (triple) bond created by the side-to-side overlap of sp^2 orbitals on adjacent carbons of the ring.

Bicyclic – a molecule with two rings that share at least two carbons.

Bimolecular reaction – two species (e.g., molecules, ions, radicals) react to form new chemical species; most reactions are bimolecular or proceed through a series of bimolecular steps.

Bond angle – the angle formed between two adjacent bonds on the same atom.

Bond-dissociation energy – the amount of energy needed to homolytically fracture a bond.

Bond energy – the energy required to break a particular bond by a homolytic process.

Bond length – the equilibrium distance between the nuclei of two atoms or groups bonded to each other.

Bond strength – see *bond-dissociation energy.*

Bonding electron – see *valence electrons.*

Bonding molecular orbital – formed by the overlap of adjacent atomic orbitals.

Branched-chain *Alkane* – an *alkane* with *alkyl groups* bonded to the central carbon chain.

Brønsted-Lowry theory of acids and bases – a compound capable of donating a proton (a hydrogen ion); a Brønsted-Lowry base can accept a hydrogen ion; in *neutralization,* an acid donates a proton to a base, creating a conjugate acid and a conjugate base.

Buffer solution – a solution of definite pH made so that the pH alters only gradually by adding an acid or base.

C

Canonical structures – any of two or more hypothetical structures of *resonance* theory which can be written for a molecule simply by rearranging the valence electrons of the molecule (e.g., the two Kekule structures of benzene); sometimes called "valence bond isomers."

Carbanion – a carbon atom bearing a negative charge; a carbon anion.

Carbene – a reactive intermediate, characterized by a neutral, electron-deficient carbon center with two substituents - two single bonds and just six electrons in its valence shell ($R_2C{:}$).

Carbenoid – a chemical that resembles a carbene in its chemical reactions.

Carbocation – a carbon *Cation*; a carbon atom bearing a positive charge (sometimes referred to as a "carbonium ion").

Carbonyl group – a carbon double bonded to oxygen (C=O).

Carboxylic acid – a molecule containing a carboxyl (~COOH) group; also, a functional group.

$$-\overset{\displaystyle \underset{\|}{\text{C}}}{\underset{\text{O}}{}}-\text{OH}$$

Catalyst – a substance that, when added to a reaction mixture, changes (speeds up) the rate of attainment of equilibrium in the system without itself undergoing a permanent chemical change.

Catalytic cracking – the method for producing gasoline from heavy petroleum distillates; generally, the catalysts are mixtures of silica and alumina or synthetic conjugates, such as zeolites.

Catalytic reforming – the process of improving the octane number of straight-run gasoline by increasing the proportion of *aromatic* and *branched-chain alkanes*; catalysts employed are either molybdenum-aluminum oxides or platinum-based.

Cation – a positively charged ion.

Cationic polymerization – occurs *via* a cation intermediate and is less efficient than *free-radical polymerization*.

Chain reaction – once started, produces enough energy to keep the reaction running; proceed by a series of steps which produce intermediates, energy, and products (e.g., the free radical addition of hydrogen bromide (HBr) to an *alkene)*.

Chair conformation – typically, the most stable cyclohexane conformation; looks like a chair.

Chemical shift – the location of an NMR peak relative to the standard tetramethylsilane (TMS), given in units of parts per million (ppm).

Chiral – describes a molecule that is not superimposable on its mirror image, like the relationship of a left hand to a right hand; see *chiral molecule.*

Chiral center – a carbon or other atom with four non-identical substituents.

Chiral molecule – a molecule that is not superimposable on its mirror image; rotate plane-polarized light.

Chirality – any asymmetric object or molecule; the property of non-identity of an object with its mirror image.

Chromatography – a series of related techniques for separating a mixture of compounds by their distribution between two phases; in gas-liquid chromatography, the distribution is between a gaseous and a liquid phase; in column chromatography, the distribution is between a liquid and a solid phase.

Cis – two identical substituents on the same side of a double bond or ring.

Closed-shell electron configuration – a stable electron configuration in which the electrons are in the lowest energy orbitals available.

Competing reactions – two reactions that start with the same reactants but form different products.

Compound – a term used generally to indicate a definite combination of elements into a more complex structure (a molecule); also applied to systems with non-stoichiometric proportions of elements.

Concerted – taking place at the same time without forming an intermediate.

Condensation reaction – a reaction in which two molecules join with the liberation of a small stable molecule.

Configuration – the order and relative three-dimensional orientation of the atoms in a molecule; given the designation R or S; "absolute configuration" is when the relative three-dimensional arrangement in the space of atoms in a *chiral* molecule has been correlated with an absolute standard.

Configurational isomers – a series of compounds that have the same constitution and bonding of atoms, but which differ in their atomic spatial arrangement (e.g., glucose and mannose).

Conformation – the spatial arrangement of a molecule in space at any moment; most molecules can adopt an infinite number of conformations because of rotation about single covalent bonds; of these possibilities, most compounds spend the most time in one or a few *preferred conformations.*

Conformer – a conformation of a molecule; generally, these will be at energy minima.

Conjugate acid – the acid that results when a Brønsted-Lowry base accepts a hydrogen ion.

Conjugate base – the base that results when a Brønsted-Lowry acid loses a hydrogen ion.

Conjugated double bonds – double bonds separated by a carbon-carbon single bond; alternating double bonds.

Conjugation – the overlapping in all directions of a series of p orbitals; a sequence of alternating double (or triple) and single bonds (e.g., C=C–C=C and C=C–C=O); can be relayed by the participation of lone pairs of electrons or vacant orbitals.

Conjugation energy – see *resonance energy*.

Constitution – the number and type of atoms in a molecule.

Constitutional isomers – molecules with the same molecular formula but with atoms attached differently.

Coordinate bond – the linkage of two atoms by a pair of electrons, both electrons provided by one of the atoms (the donor); covalent bonds.

Coupling constant (J) – the distance between two neighboring lines in an NMR peak (given in units of Hz); the separation in frequency units between multiple peaks in one chemical shift; this separation results from the spin-spin coupling.

Coupling protons – protons interacting and splitting the NMR peak into some lines following the $n+1$ rule.

Covalent bond – a bond formed by the sharing of electrons between atoms.

Cyano group – the ~C≡N group.

Cyanohydrin – a compound with the general formula:

$$
\begin{array}{c}
\text{OH} \\
| \\
\text{R}-\text{C}-\text{C}\equiv\text{N} \\
| \\
\text{R'}
\end{array}
$$

Cyclization – the forming of ring structures.

Cycloaddition – a reaction that forms a ring.

Cycloalkane – a ring hydrocarbon made of carbon and hydrogen atoms joined by single bonds.

Cycloalkyl *Alkane* – an *alkane* to which a ring structure is bonded.

Cyclohydrocarbon – an *alkane*, *alkene* or *alkyne* formed in a ring structure rather than a straight or branched chain; the general formula is C_nH_{2n} (*n* must be a whole number of 3 or greater).

D

Deactivating group – causes an *Aromatic* ring to become less reactive toward electrophilic aromatic substitution.

Debye unit (D) – the unit of measure for a dipole moment; one debye equals 1.0×10^{-18} electrostatic units (esu · cm); see *dipole moment*.

Decarboxylation – a reaction in which carbon dioxide is expelled from a carboxylic acid.

Dehalogenation – the elimination reaction in which two halogen atoms are removed from adjacent carbon atoms to form a double bond.

Dehydration – the elimination reaction in which water is removed from a molecule.

Dehydrohalogenation – the elimination reaction in which a hydrogen atom and a halogen atom (a hydrohalic acid, like HBr, HCl) are removed from a molecule to form a double bond.

Delocalization – electron systems in which bonding electrons are not localized between two atoms as for a single bond but are spread (delocalized) over the whole group (e.g., *pi-bond* electrons the delocalized pi-electrons associated with *aromatic* molecules).

Delocalization energy – see *resonance energy*.

Delta value (δ value) – the chemical shift; the location of an NMR peak relative to the reference standard tetramethylsilane (TMS), given in units of parts per million (ppm).

Deprotonation – the loss of a proton (hydrogen ion) from a molecule.

Deshielding – an effect in NMR spectroscopy that the movement of *sigma* and *pi* electrons within the molecule causes; causes chemical shifts to appear at lower magnetic fields (downfield).

Dextrorotatory – the phenomenon in which plane-polarized light is turned in a clockwise direction.

Diastereomers (diastereoisomers) – stereoisomeric structures which are not enantiomers (mirror images); often applied to systems that differ in the configuration at one carbon (e.g., *meso-* and *d-* or *l*-tartaric acids).

Diels-Alder reaction – a cycloaddition between a conjugated diene and an *alkene* that produces a 1,4-addition product.

Diene – a molecule that contains two alternating double bonds; also, a reactant in the *Diels-Alder reaction*.

Dienophile – a reactant in the *Diels-Alder reaction* that contains a double bond; often substituted with electron-withdrawing groups.

Dienophile – the *alkene* that adds to the *diene* in a Diels-Alder reaction.

Dihalide – a compound that contains two halogen atoms; also called "*a dihaloalkane.*"

Dihedral angle – the angle between groups attached on adjacent carbons when viewed in a *Newman projection*.

Diol – a compound that contains two hydroxyls (~OH) groups; also called a "*dihydroxy alkane.*"

Dipole moment – a measure of the polarity of a molecule; the mathematical product of the charge in electrostatic units (ESU), and the distance that separates the two charges in centimeters (cm) (e.g., substituted *Alkyne*s have dipole moments caused by differences in electronegativity between the triple-bonded and single-bonded carbon atoms).

Disproportionation – a process in which a compound of one oxidation state changes to compounds of two or more oxidation states (e.g., $2 \, Cu^+ \rightarrow Cu + Cu^{2+}$).

Dissociation – the process whereby a molecule splits into simpler fragments that may be smaller molecules, atoms, free radicals, or ions.

Dissociation constant – the measure of the extent of dissociation, measured by the dissociation constant K. For the process:
$$AB = A + B$$

$$K = ([A] \cdot [B]) / [AB]$$

Dissymmetric – see *chiral*.

Distillation – the separation of components of a liquid mixture based on differences in boiling points.

Double bond – some atoms can share two pairs of electrons to form a double bond (two covalent bonds); formally, the second (double) bond arises from the overlap of *p* orbitals from two atoms, already united by a *sigma* bond, to form a *pi bond*; hydrocarbons that contain one double bond are *alkenes,* and hydrocarbons with two double bonds are *dienes.*

Doublet – describes an NMR signal split into two peaks.

Dyestuffs – intensely colored compounds applied to a substrate; colors are due to the absorption of light to give electronic transitions.

E

E₁ elimination reaction – a reaction that eliminates a hydrohalic acid (e.g., HCl, HBr) to form an *alkene*; a first-order reaction that goes through a *carbocation* mechanism.

E₂ elimination reaction – a reaction that eliminates a hydrohalic acid (e.g., HCl, HBr) to form an *alkene*; a second-order reaction that occurs in a single step in which the double bond is formed as the hydrohalic acid is eliminated.

***E* isomer** – *stereoisomer* with the two highest priority groups on opposite sides of a ring or double bond.

Eclipsed – a *conformation* in which substituents on two attached saturated carbon atoms overlap when viewed as a *Newman projection*.

Eclipsed conformation – *conformation* about a carbon-carbon single bond in which the bonds off two adjacent carbons are aligned (0° apart when viewed in a *Newman projection*).

Electron – negatively charged particles of little weight that exist in quantized probability areas around the atomic nucleus.

Electron affinity – the amount of energy liberated when an electron is added to an atom in the gaseous state.

Electronegativity – measures an atom's ability to attract electrons toward itself in a covalent bond; the halogen fluorine is the most electronegative element; measured by the highest occupied molecular orbital (*HOMO*) and the lowest unoccupied molecular orbital (*LUMO*) energy levels.

Electronegativity scale – an arbitrary reference by which the electronegativity of elements can be compared.

Electronic configuration – the order in which electrons are arranged in an atom or molecule; used in a distinct and different sense from stereochemical *configuration*; see *stereochemistry*.

Electronic transition – in an atom or molecule, the electrons only have specific allowed energies (orbitals); if an electron passes from one orbital to another, an electronic transition occurs, and the emission or absorption of energy corresponds to the difference in energy of the two orbitals.

Electrophile – an "electron seeker;" an atom, molecule, or ion able to accept an electron pair to stabilize itself; a *Lewis acid*.

Electrophilic addition – a reaction in which the addition of an *electrophile* to an unsaturated molecule forms a saturated molecule.

Electrophilic substitution – an overall reaction in which an *electrophile* binds to a substrate with the expulsion of another electrophile (e.g., the electrophilic substitution of a proton by another electrophile, such as a nitronium ion, on an *Aromatic* substrate, such as benzene).

Electrostatic attraction – the attraction of a positive ion for a negative ion.

Electrovalent (ionic) bond – bonding by *electrostatic attraction*.

Element – a substance which cannot be further subdivided by chemical methods.

Element of unsaturation – a *pi bond*; a multiple bond or ring in a molecule.

Enantiomers – a pair of isomers related as mirror images of one another (e.g., isomers differing only in the configuration of the *chiral* atoms).

Enantiomorphic pair – in optically active molecules with more than one stereogenic center, the two structures are mirror images.

Endothermic – a reaction in which heat is absorbed.

Energy diagram (or *reaction energy diagram*) – a graph of the energy against the progress of the reaction.

Energy of reaction – the difference between the total energy content of the reactants and the total energy content of the products; the greater the energy of reaction, the more stable the products.

Enol – an unstable compound (e.g., *vinyl alcohol*) in which a hydroxide group is attached to a carbon in a carbon-carbon double bond; these compounds *tautomerize* to form more stable *ketones*.

Enolate ion – the resonance stabilized ion formed when an *aldehyde* or *ketone* loses an α hydrogen:

Enthalpy (*H*) – a thermodynamic state function, generally measured in kilojoules per mole; in chemical reactions, the enthalpy change (ΔH) is related to changes in the free energy (ΔG) and *entropy* (ΔS) by the equation: $\Delta G = \Delta H - T\Delta S$.

Entropy (*S*) – a thermodynamic quantity that is a measure of the degree of disorder within a system. The greater the degree of order, the higher the entropy; for an increase in entropy, *S* is positive; has the units of joules per degree K per mole.

Enzyme – a naturally occurring substance able to catalyze a chemical reaction.

Epimerization – a process in which the configuration about one *chiral* center of a compound, containing more than one *chiral* atom, is inverted to give the opposite configuration; the term "epimers" describes two related compounds that differ only in the configuration about one chiral atom.

Epoxide – a three-membered ring that contains oxygen.

Epoxidation – the addition of an oxygen bridge across a double bond to give an oxirane; achieved by use of a peracid or, in a few cases, by use of a *Catalyst* and oxygen.

Equatorial – the bonds in a chair cyclohexane oriented along the equator of the ring.

Equilibrium constant – according to the law of mass action, for a reversible chemical reaction, aA + bB = cC + dD, the equilibrium constant (*K*)is defined as: $K = ([C]^c[D]^d) / ([A]^a[B]^b)$.

Ester – a functional group; a molecule containing a carbonyl group adjacent to an oxygen (RCOOR').

$$-\overset{\displaystyle O}{\underset{\displaystyle |}{\overset{\displaystyle ||}{C}}}-OR$$

Ether – a molecule containing oxygen singly-bonded to two carbon atoms; also, a functional group; the general formula is R—O—R'; epoxyethane, an epoxide, is a cyclic ether; often refers to diethyl ether.

Excited state – the state of an atom, molecule, or group when it has absorbed energy and becomes excited to a higher energy state than the ground state; may be electronic, vibrational, rotational, etc.

F

Fischer projection – a convention for drawing carbon chains so that the relative three-dimensional stereochemistry of the carbon atoms is relatively easy to portray as a 2-dimensional drawing.

Fingerprint region – an IR spectrum below 1,500 cm^{-1}; often complex and difficult to interpret.

Free energy (ΔG) – a thermodynamic state function; the free energy change (ΔG) in any reaction is related to the *enthalpy* and *entropy*: $\Delta G = \Delta H - T\Delta S$.

Free radicals – molecules or ions with unpaired electrons; generally, extremely reactive; "stable" free radicals include molecular oxygen, NO, and NO_2; organic free radicals range from those of transient existence only to very long-lived species; alkyl free radicals tend to be very reactive and short-lived.

Free-radical chain reaction – a reaction that proceeds by a free-radical intermediate in a chain mechanism (a series of self-propagating, interconnected steps); compare with a *free-radical reaction*.

Free-radical polymerization – a polymerization initiated by a *free radical*.

Free-radical reaction – a reaction in which a covalent bond is formed by the union of two radicals; compare with a *free-radical chain reaction*.

Frontier orbital symmetry – the theory that the site and rates of reaction depend on the geometries, the sign of the wave function and relative energies of the highest occupied molecular orbital (*HOMO*) of one molecule and the lowest unoccupied molecular orbital (*LUMO*) of the other.

Functional group – a set of bonded atoms that displays a specific molecular structure and chemical reactivity when bonded to a carbon atom in the place of a hydrogen atom.

G

Gauche – a conformational isomer in which the groups are neither eclipsed nor trans to one another; often taken as the conformation where the dihedral angle between the groups is 60°.

Gauche conformation – a type of staggered conformation in which two bulky groups are next to each other.

Geometrical isomerism – isomerism from the restricted rotation about a bond (e.g., (*Z*) and (*E*) isomers of unsymmetrically substituted *alkene*s).

Grignard reagent – an organometallic reagent in which magnesium metal inserts between an *alkyl group* and a halogen (e.g., CH_3MgBr).

Ground state – the lowest energy state of an atom, molecule, or ion.

H

Half-life, $t^{1/2}$ – the time taken for the concentration of a substance in a reaction to reduce to half its original value; used in first-order reactions and as a measure of the rate of radioactive decay.

Halide – a member of the VIIA column of the periodic table (e. g., F, Cl, Br, I) or a molecule that contains one of these atoms; also, a functional group.

Haloalkane – an *alkane* that contains one or more halogen atoms; also called an *alkyl halide*.

Halogen – an electronegative, nonmetallic element in Group VII of the periodic table, including fluorine, chlorine, bromine, and iodine; often represented in structural formulas by an "X."

Halogenation – a reaction in which halogen atoms are bonded to an *Alkene* at the double bond.

Halonium ion – a halogen atom that bears a positive charge; highly unstable.

Hard and soft acids and bases – a classification of acids and bases depending on their polarizability; hard bases include fluoride ions; soft bases include triphenylphosphine; hard acids include Na^+, whilst an example of a soft, polarizable acid is Pt^{2+}; hard-hard and soft-soft interactions are favored; hardness and softness can be described in terms of the *HOMO* and *LUMO* interactions.

Heat of reaction – the amount of heat absorbed or evolved when specified amounts of compounds react under constant pressure; expressed as kilojoules per mole; for exothermic reactions, the convention is that the *Enthalpy* (*H*) change (heat of reaction) is negative.

Hemiacetal – a functional group with a hydroxyl and ether attached to the same carbon; the structure:

$$-\overset{\underset{\displaystyle H}{|}}{C}\overset{\displaystyle OR}{\underset{\displaystyle OH}{<}}$$

Hemiketal – a functional group with a hydroxyl and ether attached to the same carbon; the structure:

$$\overset{\displaystyle |}{\underset{\displaystyle R}{-C}}\!\!\begin{matrix} \nearrow OR \\ \searrow OH \end{matrix}$$

Hertz – a measure of a wave's frequency; equals the number of waves that passes a specific point per second.

Heteroatom – in organic chemistry, an atom other than carbon.

Heterocyclic compound – a class of cyclic compounds in which one of the ring atoms is not carbon (e.g., epoxyethane).

Heterogeneous reaction – occurs between substances mainly present in different phases (e.g., between a gas and a liquid).

Heterogenic bond formation – a type of bond formed by the overlap of orbitals on adjacent atoms. One orbital of the pair donates both electrons to the bond.

Heterolytic cleavage – the fracture of a bond so that one of the atoms receives both electrons; in reactions, this asymmetrical bond rupture generates carbocation and carbanion mechanism.

Heterolytic reaction – a reaction with a covalent bond broken by unequal sharing of bonding electrons.

HOMO – the highest occupied molecular orbital of a molecule, ion, or atom.

Homologous series – compounds with common compositions (e.g., *alkane*s, *alkene*s and *alkyne*s).

Homolog – one of a series of compounds in which each member differs by a constant unit.

Homolytic cleavage – the fracture of a bond in such a manner that both atoms receive one of the bond's electrons; this symmetrical bond rupture forms free radicals; in reactions, it generates *free-radical* mechanisms.

Homolytic reaction – a covalent bond is broken with equal sharing of the electrons from the bond.

Hückel's rule – a compound with $4n + 2$ π electrons has a closed-shell electron configuration and is *aromatic*.

Hybrid orbitals – formed from mixing atomic orbitals (AO), like the sp^x orbitals, which result from mixing *s* and *p* orbitals.

Hydration – the addition of the elements of water to a molecule.

Hydride shift – the movement of a hydride ion (a hydrogen atom with a negative charge; H^-) to form a more inductively-stabilized carbocation.

Hybridization – the process whereby atomic orbitals of different types but similar energies are combined to form a set of equivalent hybrid orbitals; these hybrid orbitals do not exist in the atoms but only by forming molecular orbitals by combining atomic orbitals from different atoms.

Hydroboration – the *cis*-addition of B–H bonds across double (or triple) carbon-carbon bonds.

Hydroboration-oxidation – the addition of borane (BH_3) or an alkyl borane to an *alkene* and its subsequent oxidation to produce the *anti-Markovnikov* indirect addition of water.

Hydrocarbon – a molecule that exclusively contains carbon and hydrogen atoms; the central bond may be a single, double, or triple covalent bond, and it forms the molecule's backbone.

Hydrogenation – the addition of hydrogen to a multiple bond.

Hydrogenolysis – the cleaving of a chemical bond by hydrogen, generally with a hydrogenation *catalyst*.

Hydrohalogenation – a reaction in which a hydrogen atom and a halogen atom are added to a double bond to form a saturated compound.

Hydrolysis – the addition water to a substance, often with the partition of the substance into two parts (e.g., the hydrolysis of an *ester* to an acid and an *alcohol*).

Hydrolyze – to cleave a bond *via* the elements of water.

Hyperconjugation – weak interaction (electron donation) between *sigma* bonds with *p* orbitals; explains why alkyl substituents stabilize carbocations.

I

Inductive effect – an electronic effect transmitted through bonds in an organic compound due to the electronegativity of substituents and the permanent polarization thereof; the substituent either induces charges towards or away from itself with the formation of a dipole.

Infrared spectroscopy (IR) – the study of the absorption of infrared light by substances; corresponding to vibrational (and some rotational) changes, infrared spectroscopy provides valuable information about the molecule's structure; detailed correlation tables exist relating infrared bands (absorbances) to functional groups.

Inhibitor – a general term for a compound that inhibits (slows down) a reaction; can be used to slow or stop free radical chain reactions.

Initiation step – the first step in the mechanism of a reaction.

Initiator – a material capable of being fragmented into free radicals, which initiates a *free-radical reaction*.

Insertion – placing between two atoms.

Intermediate – a species that form in one step of a multistep mechanism; unstable and cannot be isolated.

Ion – an atom or group of atoms that has lost or gained one or more electrons to become a charged species.

Ionic bond – a bond formed by the transfer of electrons between atoms, resulting in forming ions of opposite charge; the electrostatic attraction between these ions.

Ionization energy – the energy needed to remove an electron from an atom.

IR spectroscopy – an instrumental technique that measures IR (infrared) light absorption by molecules and can determine functional groups in an unknown molecule.

Isolated double bond – a double bond more than one single bond away from another double bond in a *diene*.

Isomers – compounds having the same atomic composition (*constitution*) but differing in their chemical structure; includes structural isomers (chain or positional), tautomeric isomers, and stereoisomers (including geometrical isomers, optical isomers, and conformational isomers).

IUPAC nomenclature – a systematic method for naming molecules based on a series of rules developed by the International Union of Pure and Applied Chemistry, not the only reference body, but the most common.

J

***J* value** – the coupling constant between two peaks in an NMR signal; given in units of Hz.

K

Kekulé structure – the structure for benzene in which there are three alternating double and single bonds in a six-membered ring of carbon atoms.

Ketal – the product formed by the reaction of a *ketone* with *alcohol*; the general structure is:

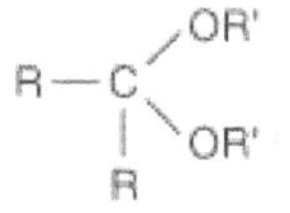

Keto-enol tautomerization – the process by which an *enol* equilibrates with its corresponding *aldehyde* or *ketone*.

Ketone – a compound in which an oxygen atom is bonded *via* a double bond to a carbon atom, bonded to two more carbon atoms.

Kinetic product – the product that forms the fastest; has the lowest *activation energy*.

Kinetics – the study of the rate of reactions.

Kinetically controlled product – the product formed from the fastest reaction in competing reaction pathways.

L

Levorotatory – the phenomenon that turns plane-polarized light in a counterclockwise direction.

LCAO – a method for calculating molecular orbitals from a "Linear Combination of Atomic Orbitals."

Leaving group – the negatively charged group that departs from a molecule undergoing a *nucleophilic substitution* reaction.

Lewis acid – an agent capable of accepting a pair of electrons to form a *coordinate bond*.

Lewis base – an agent capable of donating a pair of electrons to form a *coordinate bond*.

Lone pair – a pair of electrons in a molecule not shared by two of the constituent atoms.

Linear – the shape of a molecule with *sp* hybrid orbitals; an *alkyne*.

LUMO – the lowest unoccupied molecular orbital in a molecule or ion.

M

Markovnikov rule – the positive part of a reagent (e.g., a hydrogen atom) adds to the carbon of the double bond that already has more hydrogen atoms attached; the negative part adds to the other carbon of the double bond; leading to the more stable *carbocation* over other less-stable intermediates; useful to predict the major product; *free radical reactions* proceed in the opposite sense, giving rise to *anti-Markovnikov addition*.

Mass number – the total number of protons and neutrons in an atom.

Mass spectrometry – a form of spectrometry in which, generally, high energy electrons are bombarded onto a sample, generating charged fragments of the parent substance; electrostatic and magnetic fields then focus these ions for a spectrum of the charged fragments.

Mechanism – the series of steps that reactants go through during their conversion into products.

Meso compounds – molecules with *chiral* centers but are *achiral* due to one or more planes of symmetry.

Mesomerism – see *resonance*.

Meta – describes the positions of two substituents on a *benzene ring* separated by one carbon.

Meta-directing substituent – groups on an *aromatic* ring directing incoming *electrophiles* to meta position.

Methylene group – a ~CH_2~ group.

Microwave spectroscopy – the interaction of electromagnetic waves with wavelengths in the range 10^{-2} to 1 meter; this energy range corresponds to rotational frequencies; helpful in studying the structure of materials (generally gases) and their characterization.

Molecular ion – the fragment in a mass spectrum corresponding to the *cation* radical (M+) of the molecule; gives the molecular mass of the molecule.

Molecular orbitals – the electron orbitals belonging to a group of atoms forming a molecule.

Molecular orbital theory – a model for depicting the location of electrons that allows electrons to delocalize across the entire molecule, a more accurate but less user-friendly theory than the *valence bond theory*.

Molecule – a covalently-bonded collection of atoms with no electrostatic charge; the smallest particle of matter that can exist in a free state; in the case of ionic substances, such as sodium chloride, the molecule is considered as a pair of ions (e.g., NaCl).

Multiple bonds – a double or triple bond; atomic *p* orbitals in side-to-side overlap, preventing rotation.

Multistep synthesis – synthesis of a compound that takes several steps to achieve.

N

n+1 rule – rule for predicting the coupling for a proton in ^{1}H NMR spectroscopy; an NMR signal splits into n+1 peak, where n is the number of equivalent adjacent protons.

Natural product – a compound produced by a living organism.

Neutralization – the reaction of an acid and a base; the acid and base reaction products are salt and water.

Neutron – an uncharged particle in the atomic nucleus with the same weight as a proton; additional neutrons do not change an element but convert it to one of its isotopic forms.

Newman projection – a projection obtained by viewing along a carbon-carbon single (double) bond.

Nitrile – a compound with a cyano group (a carbon triply-bonded to nitrogen ($\sim C \equiv N$)); a functional group.

NMR – nuclear magnetic resonance spectroscopy; a technique that measures radiofrequency light absorption by molecules; a powerful structure-determining method; see *nuclear magnetic resonance spectroscopy*.

Node – a region of zero electron density in an orbital; a point of zero amplitude in a wave.

Nonbenzenoid aromatic ring – an *aromatic* ring system that does not contain a *Benzene ring*.

Nonbonding electrons – *valence electrons* not used for covalent bond formation.

Nonterminal Alkyne – an *alkyne* in which the triple bond is somewhere other than the 1 position.

Nuclear magnetic resonance (NMR) spectroscopy – a form of spectroscopy that depends on the absorption and emission of energy arising from changes in the spin states of the nucleus of an atom; for aggregates of atoms, as in molecules, minor variations in these energy changes are caused by the local chemical environment; the energy changes used are in the radiofrequency range of the electromagnetic spectrum and depend upon the magnitude of an applied magnetic field.

Nucleofuge – see *leaving group*.

Nucleophile – a "nucleus lover;" a molecule with the ability to donate a lone pair of electrons (a *Lewis base*).

Nucleophilic substitution – an overall reaction in which a *nucleophile* reacts with a compound displacing another nucleophile; such reactions commonly occur in aliphatic chemistry; if the reaction is unimolecular, they are *S_N1 reactions*; for bimolecular reactions, they are *S_N2 reactions*.

Nucleophilicity – a measure of the reactivity of a *nucleophile* in a *nucleophilic substitution* reaction.

Nucleus – the central core of an atom; the location of the protons and neutrons.

O

Optical activity – the property of certain substances to rotate plane-polarized light; associated with asymmetry; compounds that possess a *chiral* carbon atom of the same "handedness" rotate plane-polarized light; isomers that rotate light in equal but opposite directions are "optical isomers," although the better term is *enantiomers*.

Orbit – an area around an atomic nucleus with a high probability of finding an electron; also called a *shell*, divided into *orbitals* or *subshells*.

Orbital – an area in an *orbit* with a high probability of finding an electron; a "subshell;" the orbitals have the same principal and angular quantum numbers.

Organic compound – carbon-containing compound.

Ortho – describes the positions of two substituents on a *benzene ring* on adjacent carbons.

Ortho-para director – an *aromatic* substituent that directs incoming *electrophiles* to *ortho* or *para* positions.

Outer-shell electron – see *valence electrons*.

Overlap region – the region in space where atomic or molecular orbitals overlap, creating an area of high electron density.

Oxidation – a chemical process in which the proportion of electronegative substituents in a compound is increased (the loss of electrons by an atom in a covalent bond), the charge is made more positive, or the oxidation number is increased; in organic reactions, when a compound accepts additional oxygen atoms.

Oxonium ion – a positively-charged oxygen atom.

Ozonide – a compound formed by the addition of ozone to a double bond.

Ozonolysis – the cleavage of double and triple bonds by ozone, O_3.

P

Paired spin – the spinning in opposite directions of the two electrons in a bonding orbital.

Para – describes the positions of two substituents on a *benzene ring* separated by two carbons.

Parent name – the root name of a molecule according to the *IUPAC nomenclature* rules (e.g., hexane is the parent name in *trans*-1,2-dibromocyclohexane).

Peroxide – a compound that contains an oxygen-oxygen single covalent bond.

Peroxyacid – an acid of the general form:

$$R-\overset{\overset{\textstyle O}{\|}}{C}-O-OH$$

Phenyl ring – a *benzene ring* as a substituent, abbreviated Ph.

Photochemical reaction – a chemical reaction brought about by the action of light.

Pi (π) bond – formed by the side-to-side overlap of atomic *p* orbitals (with electron density above and below the two atoms, but not directly between the two atoms); weaker than a *sigma bond* because of poor orbital overlap caused by nuclear repulsion; create unsaturated molecules; found in double and triple bonds.

Pi (π) complex – an intermediate formed when a *cation* is attracted to the high electron density of a *pi bond*.

Pi (π) molecular orbital – a molecular orbital created by the side-to-side overlap of atomic *p* orbitals.

p*K*a – the scale for defining a molecule's acidity (p*K*a = –log K_a).

Plane-polarized light – light that oscillates in a single plane.

Plane of symmetry – a plane cutting through a molecule in which both halves are mirror images of each other.

Polar covalent bond – a bond in which the shared electrons are not equally available in the overlap region, forming partially positive and partially negative ends on the molecule.

Polarimeter – measures rotation of plane-polarized light by a compound, generally prepared in a solution.

Polarity – the asymmetrical distribution of electrons in a molecule, positive and negative ends on the molecule.

Precursor – the substance from which another compound is formed.

Preparation – a reaction in which the desired chemical is produced (e.g., the dehydration of an *alcohol* is a preparation for an *alkene)*.

Primary carbocation – a *carbocation* to which one *alkyl group* is bonded.

Primary (1°) carbon – a carbon atom that is attached to one other carbon atom.

Product – the substance that forms when reactants combine in a reaction.

Propagation step – the event in a free radical reaction in which both a product and energy are produced; the energy keeps the reaction going.

Protecting group – formed on a molecule by the reaction of a reagent with a substituent on the molecule; the resulting group is less sensitive to further reaction than the original group, but it must be easy to be reconverted to the original group.

Protic solvent – a solvent that contains O–H or N–H bonds.

Proton – an H^+ ion; also, a positively-charged nuclear particle.

Protonation – the addition of a proton (a hydrogen ion) to a molecule.

Pure covalent bond – in which the shared electrons are equally available to the bonded atoms.

Pyrolysis – the application of high temperatures to a compound.

R

R group – abbreviation given to an unimportant part of a molecule; indicates rest of molecule; see *alkyl group*.

Racemate – a 50:50 mixture of two enantiomers; another name for *racemic mixture*.

Racemic mixture – an equimolar mixture of the two enantiomeric isomers of a compound; because of the equal numbers of *levo-* and *dextro-*rotatory molecules present in a *racemate*, there is no net rotation of plane-polarized light (i.e., they are optically inactive).

Radical – an atom or molecule having one or more free valences; see *free radicals*.

Rate-determining step – the step in a reaction's mechanism that requires the highest activation energy and is, therefore, the slowest.

Rate of reaction – the speed with which a reaction proceeds.

Reactant – a starting material.

Reaction energy – the difference between the energy of the reactants and that of the products.

Reagent – the chemicals that ordinarily produce reaction products.

Rearrangement reaction – a reaction that causes the skeletal structure of the reactant to change in converting to product.

Reduction – chemical processes in which the proportion of more electronegative substituents is decreased, the charge is made more negative, or the oxidation number is lowered.

Resolution – the separation of a *racemate* into its two enantiomers using some *chiral* agency.

Resonance – 1) the representation of a compound by two or more canonical structures in which the *valence electrons* are rearranged to give structures of similar probability; the actual structure is a hybrid of the resonance forms; 2) the process by which a substituent removes electrons from or gives electrons to a *pi bond* in a molecule; a delocalization of electrical charge in a molecule.

Resonance energy – the difference in energy between the calculated energy content of a *resonance structure* and the actual energy content of the hybrid structure.

Resonance hybrid – the actual structure of a molecule that shows resonance; possesses the characteristics of possible structures (and consequently cannot be drawn); lower in energy than any structure for the molecule and is more stable.

Resonance structures – intermediate structures of one molecule that differ only in the positions of their electrons; used to depict the location of *pi* and nonbonding electrons on a molecule; a molecule looks like a hybrid of all resonance structures; none of the drawn resonance structures are correct, and the best representation is a hybrid of the drawn structures.

Reversible process – the forward reaction can reach an equilibrium with the reverse reaction.

Ring structure – a molecule in which the end atoms have bonded, forming a ring rather than a straight chain.

Rotamers – isomers formed by restricted rotation.

Rotation – the ability of carbon atoms attached by single bonds to freely turn, which gives the molecule an infinite number of *conformations*.

R/S convention – a formal non-ambiguous nomenclature system for assigning absolute configuration of structure to *chiral* atoms using the Cahn, Ingold and Prelog priority rules.

S

s-*cis* conformation – a relationship in which the two double bonds of a conjugated *diene* are on the same side (*cis*) of the carbon-carbon single bond connecting them; the required conformation for the *Diels-Alder reaction*.

s-*trans* conformation – the *conformation* in which the two double bonds of a conjugated *diene* are on opposite (*trans*) sides of the carbon-carbon single bond that connects them.

Saturated – the term given to organic molecules that contain no multiple bonds.

Saturated compound – a compound containing single bonds.

Saturation – the condition of a molecule containing the most atoms possible; a molecule with single bonds.

Sawhorse projection – the sideways projection of a carbon-carbon single bond and the attached substituents; gives a clearer representation of stereochemistry than the *Fischer projection*; see *Newman projection*.

Secondary carbocation – a positively charged intermediate to which two *alkyl group*s are bonded.

Secondary (2°) carbon – a carbon atom that is directly attached to two other carbon atoms.

Separation technique – a process by which products are isolated from each other and impurities.

Shielding – an effect, in NMR spectroscopy, caused by the movement of *sigma* and *pi* electrons within the molecule; causes chemical shifts to appear at higher magnetic fields (upfield).

Sigma **(σ) antibonding molecular orbital** – in which one or more electrons are less stable than when localized in the isolated atomic orbitals from which the molecular orbital (MO) was formed.

Sigma **(σ) bond** – formed by the linear combination of orbitals so that the maximum electron density is along a line joining the two nuclei of the atoms.

Sigma **(σ) bonding molecular orbital** – when electrons are more stable than localized in the isolated atomic orbitals from which the molecular orbital was formed.

Singlet – describes an NMR signal consisting of only one peak.

Skeletal structure – the carbon backbone of a molecule.

S$_N$1 – a *substitution reaction* mechanism in which the slow step is a self-ionization of a molecule to form a *carbocation*; the rate-controlling step is unimolecular.

S$_N$1 reaction – a first-order substitution reaction that goes through a *carbocation* intermediate.

S$_N$2 – a *substitution reaction* mechanism in which the rate-controlling step is a simultaneous attack by a *Nucleophile* and a departure of a *leaving group* from a molecule; the rate-controlling step is bimolecular.

S$_N$2 reaction – a second-order *substitution reaction* that takes place in one step and has no intermediates during the reaction pathway.

sp **hybrid orbital** – a molecular orbital (MO) created by combining wave functions of an *s* and a *p* orbital.

sp^2 **hybrid orbital** – a molecular orbital (MO) created by combining wave functions of an *s* and two *p* orbitals.

sp^3 **hybrid orbital** – a molecular orbital (MO) created by combining wave functions of an *s* and three *p* orbitals.

Spectrometer – an instrument that measures the spectrum of a sample (e.g., a *mass spectrometer*).

Spectrophotometer – an instrument that measures the degree of absorption (or emission) of electromagnetic radiation by a substance. The measuring system generally includes a photomultiplier UV., IR, visible and microwave regions of the electromagnetic spectrum.

Spin-spin splitting – NMR (nuclear magnetic resonance) signals caused by the coupling of nuclear spins on neighboring nonequivalent hydrogens.

Stability constant – when a complex is formed between a metal ion and a ligand in solution, the equilibrium may be expressed by a constant related to the free energy change for the process: $M + A = MA : \Delta G = -RT\ln K$.

Staggered conformation – the orientation about a carbon-carbon single bond in which bonds off one carbon are at a maximum distance apart from bonds coming from an adjacent carbon (60° apart when viewed in a *Newman projection*).

Stereochemistry – the study of the spatial arrangements of atoms in molecules and complexes.

Stereoisomers – molecules that have the same atom connectivity but different orientations of those atoms in three-dimensional space. Another name for *configurational isomer*.

Stereospecific reactions – bonds are broken and made at a particular carbon atom and lead to a single stereoisomer; if the configuration is altered in the process, the reaction undergoes inversion of configuration; if the configuration remains the same, the transformation occurs with retention of configuration.

Steric hindrance – a physical blockage of a site within a molecule by the presence of local atoms or groups of atoms; therefore, a reaction at a particular site will be impeded.

Straight-chain alkane – a saturated hydrocarbon that has no carbon-containing side chains.

Structural isomer (or *constitutional isomer*) – have the same molecular formula but different bonding among their atoms (e.g., C_4H_{10} can be butane or 2-methylpropane, and C_4H_8 can be 1-butene or 2-butene).

Subatomic particles – a component of an atom; a proton, neutron, or electron.

Substituent – a piece that sticks off the main carbon chain or ring.

Substituent group – an atom or group that replaces a hydrogen atom on a hydrocarbon.

Substitution – the replacement of an atom or group bonded to a carbon atom with a second atom or group.

Substitution reactions – an atom or group of atoms replace one atom or group of atoms; see *electrophilic substitutions* and *nucleophilic substitutions*.

Syn addition – a reaction in which two groups of a reagent X–Y add on the same face of a carbon-carbon double bond.

T

Tautomerism – a form of structural isomerism where the two structures are interconvertible using the migration of a proton.

Tautomers – molecules that differ in the placement of hydrogen and double bonds and are easily interconvertible; keto and *enol* forms are tautomers; see *keto-enol tautomerization*.

Terminal alkyne – an *alkyne* whose triple bond is between the first and second carbon atoms of the chain.

Terminal carbon – the carbon atom on the end of a carbon chain.

Termination step – the step in a reaction mechanism ending the reaction, often between two free radicals.

Tertiary carbocation – a *carbocation* to which three *alkyl group*s are bonded.

Tertiary (3°) carbon – a carbon atom that is directly attached to three other carbon atoms.

Tetrahaloalkane – an *alkane* that contains four halogen atoms on the carbon chain; the halogen atoms can be on vicinal or non-vicinal carbon atoms.

Thermodynamic product – the reaction product with the lowest energy.

Thermodynamically controlled reaction – conditions permit two or more products to form; the products are in an equilibrium condition, allowing the more stable product to predominate.

Thermodynamics – the study of the energies of molecules.

Thiol – a molecule containing an –SH group; also, a functional group.

Tosyl group – a *p*-toluenesulfonate group:

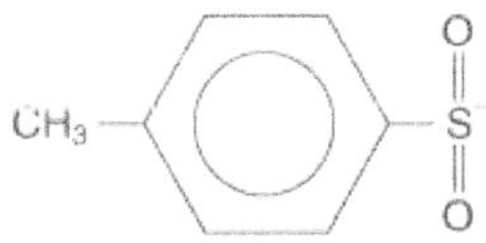

Tosylation – a reaction that introduces the toluene-4-sulphonyl group into a molecule, generally by reacting an *alcohol* with tosyl chloride to give the tosylate *ester*.

Transition state – the point of highest energy on an energy against reaction coordinate curve; the least stable point (peak) on a reaction path; a reaction path may involve more than one transition state.

Trigonal planar – the shape of a molecule with an sp^2 hybrid orbital; in this arrangement, the *sigma bonds* are in a single plane separated by 60° angles.

Triple bond – a multiple bond composed of one *sigma bond* and two *pi bond*s; rotation is not possible around a triple bond; hydrocarbons containing triple bonds are *alkyne*s.

Triplet – describes an NMR signal split into three peaks.

U

Ultraviolet light (UV) – radiation of a higher energy range than visible light but lower than that of ionizing radiations (e.g., X-rays); many substances absorb ultraviolet light, leading to electronic excitation; useful both for characterizing materials and stimulating chemical reactions (*photochemical reactions*).

Ultraviolet spectroscopy – spectroscopy that measures how much energy a molecule absorbs in the ultraviolet region of the spectrum.

Unsaturated – an organic compound containing multiple bonds.

Unsaturated compound – contain one or more multiple bonds (e.g., *alkene*s and *alkyne*s).

Unsaturation – a molecule containing less than the maximum number of single bonds due to multiple bonds.

V

Valence bond theory – the mechanical wave basis of *resonance* theory.

Valence electrons – the outermost electrons of an atom (e.g., the valence electrons of the carbon atom occupy the $2s$, $2p_x$ and $2p_y$ orbitals).

Valence isomerization – the isomerization of molecules that involve structural changes resulting only from a relocation of single and double bonds; if a dynamic equilibrium is established between the two isomers, it is referred to as "valence *tautomerism*" (e.g., the valence tautomerism of cyclo-octa-1,3,5-triene).

Valence shell – the outermost electron orbit.

Vinyl alcohol – ~CH_2=CH–OH

Vinyl group – the ethenyl group: ~CH=CH_2.

W

Walden inversion – a Walden inversion occurs at a tetrahedral carbon atom during an *S_N2 reaction* when the entry of the reagent and the departure of the leaving group are synchronous; the result is an inversion of configuration at the center under attack.

Wurtz reaction – the coupling of two *alkyl halide* molecules to form an *alkane*.

X

X group – "X" is the abbreviation for a halogen substituent in the structural formula of an organic molecule.

Y

Ylide – a neutral molecule in which two oppositely charged atoms are bonded to each other.

Z

Z isomer – the two highest-priority substituents are on the same side of a double bond or ring.

Zaitsev's rule – the major product in the formation of *alkene*s by elimination reactions will be the more highly substituted alkene or the alkene with more substituents on the carbon atoms of the double bond.

Customer Satisfaction Guarantee

Your feedback is important because we strive to provide the highest quality prep materials. Email us comments or suggestions.

info@sterling–prep.com

We reply to emails – check your spam folder

Highest quality guarantee

Be the first to report a content error for a $10 reward
or a grammatical mistake to receive a $5 reward.

Thank you for choosing our book!

Periodic Table of the Elements

1 IA 1A																	18 VIIIA 8A
1 `+1,-1` **H** Hydrogen 1.008	2 IIA 2A											13 IIIA 3A	14 IVA 4A	15 VA 5A	16 VIA 6A	17 VIIA 7A	2 **He** Helium 4.003
3 `+1` **Li** Lithium 6.941	4 `+2` **Be** Beryllium 9.012											5 `+3` **B** Boron 10.811	6 `+4,+3,+2,+1` **C** Carbon 12.011	7 `+5,+4,+3` **N** Nitrogen 14.007	8 `+6,+4,-2,+1` **O** Oxygen 15.999	9 `+7,+5,+3,+1` **F** Fluorine 18.998	10 **Ne** Neon 20.180
11 `+1` **Na** Sodium 22.990	12 `+2` **Mg** Magnesium 24.305	3 IIIB 3B	4 IVB 4B	5 VB 5B	6 VIB 6B	7 VIIB 7B	8 VIII 8	9 VIII 8	10 VIII 8	11 IB 1B	12 IIB 2B	13 `+3` **Al** Aluminum 26.982	14 `+4,+2,-4` **Si** Silicon 28.086	15 `+5,+3,-3` **P** Phosphorus 30.974	16 `+6,+4,+2,-2` **S** Sulfur 32.066	17 `+7,+5,+3,+1,-1` **Cl** Chlorine 35.453	18 `+2,0` **Ar** Argon 39.948
19 `+1` **K** Potassium 39.098	20 `+2` **Ca** Calcium 40.078	21 `+3` **Sc** Scandium 44.956	22 `+4,+3` **Ti** Titanium 47.88	23 `+5,+4,+3,+2` **V** Vanadium 50.942	24 `+6,+3,+2` **Cr** Chromium 51.996	25 `+7,+4,+3,+2` **Mn** Manganese 54.938	26 `+6,+3,+2` **Fe** Iron 55.845	27 `+3,+2` **Co** Cobalt 58.933	28 `+3,+2` **Ni** Nickel 58.693	29 `+2,+1` **Cu** Copper 63.546	30 `+2` **Zn** Zinc 65.38	31 `+3` **Ga** Gallium 69.723	32 `+4,+2` **Ge** Germanium 72.631	33 `+5,+3,-3` **As** Arsenic 74.922	34 `+6,+4,-2` **Se** Selenium 78.971	35 `+5,+3,+1,-1` **Br** Bromine 79.904	36 **Kr** Krypton 84.798
37 `+1` **Rb** Rubidium 85.468	38 `+2` **Sr** Strontium 87.62	39 `+3` **Y** Yttrium 88.906	40 `+4` **Zr** Zirconium 91.224	41 `+5,+3` **Nb** Niobium 92.906	42 `+6,+4` **Mo** Molybdenum 95.95	43 `+7,+4` **Tc** Technetium 98.907	44 `+4,+3` **Ru** Ruthenium 101.07	45 `+3` **Rh** Rhodium 102.906	46 `+4,+2` **Pd** Palladium 106.42	47 `+2,+1` **Ag** Silver 107.868	48 `+2` **Cd** Cadmium 112.414	49 `+3,+1` **In** Indium 114.818	50 `+4,+2` **Sn** Tin 118.711	51 `+5,+3,-3` **Sb** Antimony 121.760	52 `+6,+4,-2` **Te** Tellurium 127.6	53 `+7,+5,+1,-1` **I** Iodine 126.904	54 `+6,+4,+2,0` **Xe** Xenon 131.294
55 `+1` **Cs** Cesium 132.905	56 `+2` **Ba** Barium 137.328	57-71	72 `+4` **Hf** Hafnium 178.49	73 `+5` **Ta** Tantalum 180.948	74 `+6` **W** Tungsten 183.85	75 `+7` **Re** Rhenium 186.207	76 `+4,+3` **Os** Osmium 190.23	77 `+4,+3` **Ir** Iridium 192.22	78 `+4,+2` **Pt** Platinum 195.08	79 `+3,+1` **Au** Gold 196.967	80 `+2,+1` **Hg** Mercury 200.59	81 `+3,+1` **Tl** Thallium 204.383	82 `+4,+2` **Pb** Lead 207.2	83 `+5,+3` **Bi** Bismuth 208.980	84 `+4,+2` **Po** Polonium [208.982]	85 `-1` **At** Astatine 209.987	86 `+2,0` **Rn** Radon 222.018
87 `+1` **Fr** Francium 223.020	88 `+2` **Ra** Radium 226.025	89-103	104 **Rf** Rutherfordium [261]	105 **Db** Dubnium [262]	106 **Sg** Seaborgium [266]	107 **Bh** Bohrium [264]	108 **Hs** Hassium [269]	109 unknown **Mt** Meitnerium [278]	110 unknown **Ds** Darmstadtium [281]	111 unknown **Rg** Roentgenium [280]	112 unknown **Cn** Copernicium [285]	113 unknown **Nh** Nihonium [286]	114 unknown **Fl** Flerovium [289]	115 unknown **Mc** Moscovium [289]	116 unknown **Lv** Livermorium [293]	117 unknown **Ts** Tennessine [294]	118 unknown **Og** Oganesson [294]

Symbol — Atomic Number / Valence / Name / Atomic Mass

Lanthanide Series	57 `+3` **La** Lanthanum 138.905	58 `+4,+3` **Ce** Cerium 140.116	59 `+3` **Pr** Praseodymium 140.908	60 `+3` **Nd** Neodymium 144.243	61 `+3` **Pm** Promethium 144.913	62 `+3` **Sm** Samarium 150.36	63 `+3,+2` **Eu** Europium 151.964	64 `+3` **Gd** Gadolinium 157.25	65 `+3` **Tb** Terbium 158.925	66 `+3` **Dy** Dysprosium 162.500	67 `+3` **Ho** Holmium 164.930	68 `+3` **Er** Erbium 167.259	69 `+3` **Tm** Thulium 168.934	70 `+3` **Yb** Ytterbium 173.055	71 `+3` **Lu** Lutetium 174.967
Actinide Series	89 `+3` **Ac** Actinium 227.028	90 `+4` **Th** Thorium 232.038	91 `+5,+4` **Pa** Protactinium 231.036	92 `+6` **U** Uranium 238.029	93 `+6` **Np** Neptunium 237.048	94 `+6` **Pu** Plutonium 244.064	95 `+3` **Am** Americium 243.061	96 `+3` **Cm** Curium 247.070	97 `+3` **Bk** Berkelium 247.070	98 `+3` **Cf** Californium 251.080	99 `+3` **Es** Einsteinium [254]	100 `+3` **Fm** Fermium 257.095	101 `+3` **Md** Mendelevium 258.1	102 `+3` **No** Nobelium 259.101	103 `+3` **Lr** Lawrencium [262]

Isomer Classification

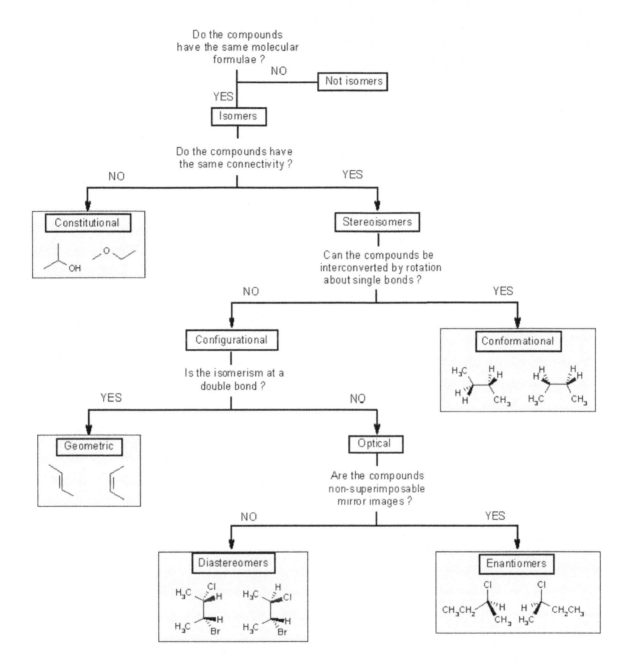

Notes for active learning

College study aids

Cell and Molecular Biology Review

Organismal Biology Review

Cell and Molecular Biology Practice Questions

Organismal Biology Practice Questions

Physics Review (Part 1 and 2)

Physics Practice Questions (Vol. 1 and 2)

United States History 101

American Government and Politics 101

Environmental Science 101

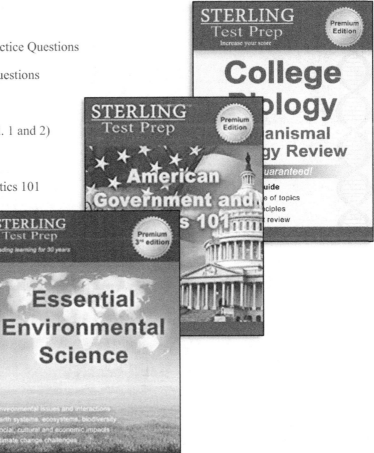

College Level Examination Program (CLEP)

Visit our Amazon store

Frank J. Addivinola, Ph.D.

The lead author and chief editor of this study guide is Dr. Frank Addivinola. With his outstanding education, laboratory research, and decades of university science teaching, Dr. Addivinola lent his expertise to develop this book.

Dr. Frank Addivinola conducted original research in developmental biology as a doctoral candidate and pre-IRTA fellow in Molecular and Cell Biology at the National Institutes of Health (NIH). His dissertation advisor was Nobel laureate Marshall W. Nirenberg, Chief of the Biochemical Genetics Laboratory at the National Heart, Lung, and Blood Institute (NHLBI). Before NIH, Dr. Addivinola researched prostate cancer in the Cell Growth and Regulation Laboratory of Dr. Arthur Pardee at the Dana Farber Cancer Institute of Harvard Medical School.

Dr. Addivinola holds an undergraduate degree in biology from Williams College. He completed his Masters at Harvard University, Masters in Biotechnology at Johns Hopkins University, and five other graduate degrees at the University of Maryland University College, Suffolk University, and Northeastern University.

During his extensive teaching career, Dr. Addivinola taught numerous undergraduate and graduate-level courses, including biology, biochemistry, organic chemistry, inorganic chemistry, anatomy and physiology, medical terminology, nutrition, and medical ethics. He received several awards for his research and presentations.

Made in the USA
Coppell, TX
16 June 2023